FOOD FOR
HEALTH
& FITNESS

Helen O'Connor
and Donna Hay

CONTENTS

UK COOKERY EDITOR
Katie Swallow

EDITORIAL
Food Editor: Rachel Blackmore
Subeditor: Ella Martin
Editorial Assistant: Sheridan Packer
Editorial Coordinator: Margaret Kelly

PHOTOGRAPHY
Quentin Bacon

DESIGN AND PRODUCTION
Manager: Sheridan Carter
Layout and Design: Gavin Murrell
Cover: Frank Pithers

ACKNOWLEDGMENTS
The authors and publisher wish to thank the following people
for their support and assistance with this book.
Models: Jason Mitchell, Andrew Simmons,
Consultant Dietitians: Maureen O'Connor, Soumella Amanatidis
Brad Childs for his continual support and many hours of typing

Published by J.B. Fairfax Press Pty Limited
A.C.N. 003 738 430
Formatted by J.B. Fairfax Press Pty Limited
Printed by Toppan Printing Co, Hong Kong

JBFP 234 UK
Includes Index
ISBN 1 86343 129 2

Distributed by J.B. Fairfax Press Ltd
9 Trinity Centre, Park Farm Estate
Wellingborough, Northants, UK
Ph: (0933) 402330 Fax: (0933) 402234

About this Book

Nutritional analysis

Each recipe has been computer analysed for its kilojoule (calorie), fat and carbohydrate content. Based on the amount of fat and the percentage of energy from carbohydrate, the recipes have been rated according to the following guidelines:

Carbohydrate

Rated on the percentage of energy (kilojoules/calories) from carbohydrate:

less than 50%	low
50-55%	medium
56-69%	high
70% or more	very high

Fat

Rated on the grams of fat per serving:

less than 5 g	very low
5 g to less than 10 g	low
10-15 g	medium
more than 15 g	high

The pantry shelf

Unless otherwise stated, the following ingredients used in this book are:
Flour – White flour, plain or standard
Sugar – White sugar

What's in a tablespoon?

Australia:
   1 tablespoon = 20 mL or
   4 teaspoons
New Zealand:
   1 tablespoon = 15 mL or
   3 teaspoons
United Kingdom:
   1 tablespoon = 15 mL or
   3 teaspoons

The recipes in this book were tested in Australia where a 20 mL tablespoon is standard. All measures are level.

The tablespoon in the New Zealand and United Kingdom sets of measuring spoons is 15 mL. In many recipes this difference will not matter. For recipes using baking powder, gelatine, bicarbonate of soda, and small quantities of flour and cornflour, simply add another teaspoon for each tablespoon specified.

THE AUTHORS

HELEN O'CONNOR is a sports dietitian, with a Bachelor of Science from The University of New South Wales and a Post-Graduate Diploma in Nutrition and Dietetics.

Helen has been practising as a dietitian for the past ten years and for eight of these has specialised in sports nutrition. She is currently consultant to the Sports Science and Research Centre, Sydney University, and the New South Wales Academy of Sport. She is also chairperson for the Sports Nutrition Interest Group of the Australian Sports Medicine Federation and is an active member of the Women in Sports Committee. She is personal dietitian to the world champion boxer Jeff Harding, a number of Australia's elite athletes and works closely with teams and sportspeople who are involved in all sports at both amateur and professional levels.

Helen has had a lifelong interest in sport which has included ballet dancing, playing both tennis and squash at a competitive level and teaching ballet and aerobics.

DONNA HAY is a young freelance home economist and food stylist who trained at East Sydney Technical College. She is currently a consultant to the New South Wales Academy of Sport and to a number of Australian publishers.

Donna has worked in various areas of the food industry since she was sixteen and for the past four years as a home economist. She brings a fresh approach to both food and food presentation.

For Donna, the challenge of this book was to develop recipes that used a minimum of fat while retaining flavour. Recipes such as the Chocolate Brownies, the Mango Cheesecake and the Strawberry Sponge demonstrate just how well she has managed to achieve this.

Donna's interest in sport includes playing representative hockey.

Helen and Donna regularly lecture to sportspeople on cooking and nutrition and it was as a result of these lectures that they saw a need for a book that puts into practise what they and other health professionals are teaching. They have combined their talents to write this book.

INTRODUCTION

As sport becomes increasingly more competitive, athletes are realising that what they eat is as important to their performance as are their training methods; in fact what they eat is an essential part of the overall training programme.

The recipes and information in this book will be of interest and benefit to both amateur and professional athletes. The Taste of Fitness shows that the discipline required to follow a healthy diet need not be difficult and that a good diet will restrict you from very few food types – just wait until you see some of the recipes.

Research shows that a diet low in fat and high in complex carbohydrates is ideal for the competitive sportsperson. Other factors such as carbohydrate (glycogen) loading prior to competition and eating for recovery are also important factors in ensuring that athletes reach and stay in peak condition.

In this book you will find up-to-date nutritional information presented in a clear and easy-to-understand way. The quizzes are fun to do and show you very quickly where and how to improve your eating habits. The question-and-answer format addresses those questions most often asked by athletes. It should also be remembered that, while the book is primarily aimed at sportspeople, the recipes are suitable for anyone wanting healthy, easy-to-prepare food.

The Taste of Fitness is a must for any sportsperson's library. Remember what you eat will make a difference to your performance and may just give you that winning edge.

INFORMATION FOR BRITISH READERS

Cheese: In this book a variety of reduced- and low-fat cheeses have been used. If any of these are unavailable you can substitute a similar reduced- or low-fat variety. In the case of low-fat ricotta cheese simply use regular ricotta cheese. (Regular ricotta cheese is a medium-fat cheese, the low-fat variety is made with skimmed milk.) If you need to use a substitute, remember that this may alter the nutritional analysis of the recipe.

Canned salmon and tuna: The recipes that use canned salmon and tuna state that these should be canned in water; this is to reduce salt intake. However, if this product is not available, use canned salmon or tuna in brine, drain it well, rinse it under cold running water and then drain again before using.

Sports drinks: The sports drinks referred to in this book are glucose polymer drinks. If the brands mentioned are unavailable, any other glucose polymer drink can be used in its place. Your local supplier or nutritionist will be able to advise you on which is most suitable for your needs.

A BALANCED DIET
THE KEY TO SUCCESS

Forget what you've heard about good and bad foods. Balanced eating means that you can eat all foods – it's just that it's best if you eat more of some than others. Is your diet well balanced? Do this quiz and find out how well you score.

NUTRITION CHECK LIST

		Yes	No
1	I eat at least 3-4 slices of bread a day. (1 roll = 2 slices of bread)	☐	☐
2	I eat one serve of breakfast cereal each day – or an extra slice of bread.	☐	☐
3	I eat at least one piece of fruit each day.	☐	☐
4	I mostly eat wholegrain breads and cereals.	☐	☐
5	I eat at least 3 vegetables or have a salad most days.	☐	☐
6	I eat at least 1 and usually 2 serves of meat or meat alternative (poultry, seafood, eggs or dried peas/beans, nuts) each day.	☐	☐
7	I spread butter or margarine thinly on bread or use none at all.	☐	☐
8	I fry no more than once a week.	☐	☐
9	I use only polyunsaturated or mono-unsaturated oil (canola or olive oil) for cooking. (Tick YES if you never fry in oil or fat.)	☐	☐
10	I avoid oil-based dressings on salads.	☐	☐
11	I use reduced-fat dairy products.	☐	☐
12	I cut the fat off meat and take the skin off chicken.	☐	☐
13	I drink no more than 4 cups of tea, coffee, hot chocolate, coke or caffeine-containing drinks each day.	☐	☐
14	I avoid adding salt to my food.	☐	☐
15	I eat fatty snacks such as chocolate, chips etc. no more than once a week.	☐	☐
16	I eat 3 serves of dairy food or soy milk alternative each day. 1 serve = 200 mL/6$\frac{1}{2}$ fl oz milk; 1 slice (30 g/1 oz) hard cheese; 200 g/6$\frac{1}{2}$ oz yogurt; or 200 mL/6$\frac{1}{2}$ fl oz fortified soy milk.	☐	☐
17	I would skip a breakfast, lunch or dinner meal, no more than once a week.	☐	☐
18	I am aware of the best sources of iron and try to include an iron-rich food in my diet each day. (See page 43 for information on iron-rich foods.)	☐	☐
19	When I drink alcohol, I would mostly drink no more than 2 standard drinks (see page 36 for information on what is a standard drink) on any day and would rarely drink alcohol more than is recommended as the safe drink driving limit. (Score a point if you don't drink alcohol.)	☐	☐
20	I eat fast/takeaway food no more than once a week.	☐	☐

TOTAL _____

Scoring: For each YES answer score 1 point.

18 or more	Excellent
15–17	Room for improvement
12–14	Just made it
less than 12	Poor

Very active people will need to eat more breads, cereals and fruit than indicated in this quiz, but to stay healthy no one should be eating less. Use this quiz as a personal nutrition check list or to rate a diet you may read in a book or magazine. It will help you to sort out the good diets from the fad diets.

The Winning Plate

The typical home-cooked meal may look wholesome, but the proportions of nutrients eaten by most people in the Western world are unbalanced. We eat too much fat and not enough complex carbohydrate or fibre.

TYPICAL PLATE

Dietary Analysis
Protein 10-15%
Fat 40%
Carbohydrate 50%

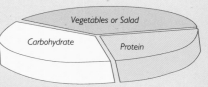

▶ *Carbohydrate serve too small*
▶ *Fat often added to carbohydrate serve*
e.g. fried chips, fried rice, excess butter on bread, cream sauce on pasta
▶ *Fibre content of meal not enough, sometimes no vegetables or salad at all*
▶ *Vegetables often overcooked or cooked with added fat*
▶ *Salads often served with an oil-based dressing*
▶ *Protein portion often cooked in fat*
▶ *Fatty meat, poultry with skin, or fried seafood add more fat to the meal*

WINNING PLATE

Dietary Analysis
Protein 10-15%
Fat 20-25%
Carbohydrate 60-70%

▶ *High-carbohydrate and high-fibre foods, such as bread, pasta, rice or potatoes, make up 60-70% of the meal*
▶ *Choose lean meats*
▶ *Remove fat and skin from poultry*
▶ *Grill, steam, dry-fry or bake meat, poultry and seafood. Avoid cooking in fat*
▶ *Generous serve of high-fibre foods, such as vegetables or salads, prepared without fat*

To maintain good health and improve physical performance, we need to turn the tables on our current food habits and practices. We can make a start by altering the proportions of food on our plate.

Plates Pillivuyt

BREAKFAST
FUELLING FOR THE DAY AHEAD

Banana Porridge

Serves 2

2 cups/500 mL/16 fl oz skim milk
2 cups/185 g/6 oz rolled oats
2 bananas, roughly chopped
1/2 teaspoon ground cinnamon (optional)

1   Place milk in a saucepan and heat, stirring occasionally, over a medium heat for 1-2 minutes or until hot.

2   Stir in rolled oats and cook, stirring constantly, for 2-3 minutes or until oats are soft. Add banana and mix to combine.

3   Spoon porridge into serving bowls, sprinkle with cinnamon and top with 3/4 cup/185 mL/6 fl oz skim milk.

Microwave it: Place milk in a microwave-safe container and cook on HIGH (100%) for 1 minute, stir in rolled oats and cook on HIGH (100%) for 1 minute longer. Stir in banana, sprinkle with cinnamon and serve.

1265 kilojoules (300 Calories) per serve
Carbohydrate   52.5 g (69%)   high
Fat   4 g   very low

Apple and Sultana Porridge

Replace banana with 1 grated apple and 3 tablespoons sultanas.

1285 kilojoules (305 Calories) per serve
Carbohydrate   55 g (70%)   very high
Fat   4 g   very low

Pear and Yogurt Porridge

Replace banana with 1 roughly chopped pear and instead of serving with milk, serve with 1/2 cup/125 g/4 oz low-fat natural, vanilla or fruit-flavoured yogurt.

1020 kilojoules (265 Calories) per serve
Carbohydrate   43.5 g (64%)   high
Fat   4 g   very low

Fast Frittata

Serves 2

2 slices reduced-fat-and-salt ham, chopped
1/2 red pepper, sliced
1 tomato, chopped
1 small zucchini (courgette), cut into strips
2 eggs, lightly beaten
3/4 cup/185 mL/6 fl oz reduced-fat milk
1/2 teaspoon dried mixed herbs or
1 tablespoon chopped fresh herbs of your choice
freshly ground black pepper

1   Place ham, red pepper, tomato and zucchini (courgette) in a small nonstick frying pan and cook over a medium heat for 2-3 minutes or until vegetables are soft.

2   Place eggs, milk, herbs and black pepper to taste in a bowl and whisk to combine.

3   Pour egg mixture over vegetable mixture and cook over a low heat for 3-4 minutes or until frittata is set.

4   Place frittata under a preheated hot grill and cook for 1 minute or until top is browned. Serve hot with toast.

Lunchbox idea: Frittata is also delicious eaten cold. Allow to cool, then wrap in plastic food wrap. The frittata will keep in the refrigerator for up to 3 days.

615 kilojoules (145 Calories) per serve
Carbohydrate   8 g (20%)   low
Fat   6 g   low

Magic Muesli

Serves 2

2 cups/250 g/8 oz untoasted muesli
4 cups/1 litre/1 3/4 pt skim milk or orange juice

Place muesli in a bowl, pour over milk or orange juice, cover and refrigerate overnight. Serve cold or heat and eat warm.

To heat: Place muesli mixture in a saucepan and cook, stirring, over a medium heat for 4-5 minutes or until heated through.

Microwave it: Remove cover from bowl and cook on HIGH (100%) for 4-5 minutes. Stir after 2 minutes. Remember to use a microwave-safe bowl.

1240 kilojoules (295 Calories) per serve with milk
Carbohydrate   45 g (59%)   high
Fat   6 g   low

1230 kilojoules (295 Calories) per serve with juice
Carbohydrate   51 g (69%)   high
Fat   6 g   low

Ham and Egg Pie

Serves 4
Oven temp: 180°C, 350°F, Gas 4

6 slices white or wholemeal bread, crusts removed
4 slices reduced-fat-and-salt ham, chopped
3 eggs, lightly beaten
1 teaspoon wholegrain mustard
1 1/2 cups/375 mL/12 fl oz reduced-fat milk
30 g/1 oz grated reduced-fat Cheddar cheese

1   Line a 20 cm/8 in square cake tin with nonstick baking paper. Line base of tin with bread slices, cutting slices to fit.

2   Heat a nonstick frying pan, add ham and cook, stirring, for 3-4 minutes or until crisp. Remove ham from pan, drain on absorbent kitchen paper and sprinkle over bread.

3   Place eggs, mustard, milk and cheese in a bowl and whisk to combine. Pour egg mixture into tin and bake for 25-30 minutes or until puffed and golden.

Cook's tip: This makes a great hot breakfast or is just as delicious cold for lunch or snacks

985 kilojoules (235 Calories) per serve
Carbohydrate   22 g (37%)   low
Fat   8 g   low

Magic Muesli, Banana Porridge, Ham and Egg Pie. Fast Frittata

The Importance of Breakfast

Breakfast is the meal which breaks the overnight fast, hence the name 'breakfast'.

Statistics worldwide show that breakfast is frequently skipped. For those of you who are tempted to skip breakfast, remember that nutrients missed at breakfast are seldom made up during the day. For active people, a good breakfast ensures that their bodies are fuelled and ready for physical activity.

The following are some of the most frequently asked questions about breakfast:

'Should I eat breakfast before or after training?'

It may be easier for early morning exercisers to eat breakfast after training. However, if you exercise strenuously for over an hour, it is best if you eat or drink something containing carbohydrate prior to training, even if it's only part of your full breakfast. Eat the rest of your breakfast after training to refuel your muscles for the day ahead. Sports drinks (see page 34), juices or reduced-fat milk drinks (page 33) are great if you find it difficult to train on a full stomach.

'I don't have time to eat breakfast in the morning. How can I catch up through the day?'

Firstly, a healthy breakfast can be fast. The recipes in this book are designed to be quick, easy to prepare as well as healthy. You only need to spend 5-10 minutes extra in the morning and for your body's sake it's worth it. If you can't manage food, try a liquid breakfast. You'll find some energising recipes in the drinks section (page 33). Have one of these drinks on the way to school or work or instead of that cup of coffee at morning tea.

Alternatively, take healthy snacks (page 13) or extra lunch (page 22) along with you so you can grab a quick bite of something healthy when you get a break through the morning.

'What should I eat for breakfast?'

The best foods to include are those which are high in carbohydrate and low in fat. Wholegrain breads and cereals, fruit and juice. Top cereal with reduced-fat milk or low-fat yogurt. Choosing a combination of these foods helps you obtain a range of nutrients. Best hot options include baked beans, spaghetti and pancakes. See recipe section for other ideas.

'I'm trying to lose weight. What should I eat for breakfast?'

Many dieters skip breakfast. Research suggests that breakfast skippers are more often overweight! Skipping breakfast makes you hungrier at other times of the day – usually between meals when it's easy to snack on foods that are high in fat and sugar. A good breakfast will keep you going for hours and helps you to control cravings for sugary or fatty foods.

'Is there anything I should avoid at breakfast?'

Sausages, bacon, fried eggs, croissants, pastries and the like are high in fat and therefore best avoided. Whilst the occasional splurge is okay, aim to keep to the cereals, breads and fruit which provide carbohydrate and a minimum of fat.

'Should breakfast be the biggest meal of the day?'

The old expression, 'Breakfast like a king, lunch like a queen and dinner like a pauper', reinforces the principle of eating substantially through the day when you are most active. If you are in heavy training, you may need three king-size meals plus snacks in between. A substantial evening meal is fine, provided you have eaten well throughout the day – don't save up a day's worth of food for just one evening meal. Eating well in the evening is vital for recovery if you train hard in the afternoon.

'How do I select the right breakfast cereal?'

Read the labels on cereal boxes. Compare the amount of fat, fibre and carbohydrate and look for the amount of sugar in the cereal. Choose varieties which are lower in sugar and higher in starch (complex carbohydrate) and fibre. Avoid toasted cereals – they are toasted in fat.

SPORTING SNACKS
TIME OUT TO TOP UP ON CARBOHYDRATE AND ENERGY

Banana Muffins

Makes 6 large muffins
Oven temp: 190°C, 375°F, Gas 5

1³/₄ cups/280 g/9 oz wholemeal self-raising flour
¹/₄ cup/15 g/¹/₂ oz skim milk powder
¹/₂ cup/100 g/3¹/₂ oz low-fat natural yogurt
1 egg
¹/₂ cup/125 mL/4 fl oz orange juice
³/₄ cup/125 g/4 oz brown sugar
¹/₄ cup/60 mL/2 fl oz water
2 large bananas, mashed
2 tablespoons sultanas
¹/₂ teaspoon ground cinnamon

1   Place flour, milk powder, yogurt, egg, orange juice, sugar, water, bananas, sultanas and cinnamon in a large bowl and mix to combine. Take care not to overmix.

2   Spoon mixture into six nonstick large muffin tins and bake for 30-35 minutes or until cooked.

1265 kilojoules (300 Calories) per muffin

Carbohydrate	62 g (80%)	very high
Fat	2 g	very low

Pumpkin Muffins

Replace bananas with 1 cup/250 g/8 oz cooked, mashed pumpkin.

1150 kilojoules (275 Calories) per muffin

Carbohydrate	55 g (78%)	very high
Fat	2 g	very low

Pineapple and Apricot Muffins

Replace bananas with 440 g/14 oz canned pineapple pieces, drained and chopped and 30 g/1 oz chopped dried apricots. Replace orange juice with apricot nectar or juice.

1090 kilojoules (260 Calories) per muffin

Carbohydrate	55 g (79%)	very high
Fat	2 g	very low

Muesli Bars

Makes 14 bars
Oven temp: 180°C, 350°F, Gas 4

2 cups/185 g/6 oz rolled oats
6 Weet-Bix (Weetabix), lightly crushed
¹/₂ cup/90 g/3 oz raisins
60 g/2 oz chopped dried apricots
¹/₂ cup/170 g/5¹/₂ oz honey
1 cup/250 mL/8 fl oz orange juice
2 egg whites

1   Place oats, Weet-Bix (Weetabix), raisins and apricots in a bowl and mix to combine.

2   Place honey and orange juice in a small saucepan and bring to the boil over a medium heat. Reduce heat and simmer for 8-10 minutes or until mixture is thick and syrupy.

3   Stir honey mixture into oats mixture, then mix in egg whites.

4   Press mixture into a nonstick 18 x 28 cm/7 x 11 in tin lined with nonstick baking paper and bake for 20-25 minutes or until golden. Cool in tin, then cut into bars and store in an airtight container.

535 kilojoules (127 Calories) per serve

Carbohydrate	26.3 g (81%)	very high
Fat	1.3 g	very low

Cheese and Chive Scones

Makes 12-14
Oven temp: 180°C, 350°F, Gas 4

3 cups/375 g/12 oz self-raising flour
30 g/1 oz grated Parmesan cheese
45 g/1¹/₂ oz grated reduced-fat Cheddar cheese
3 tablespoons snipped fresh chives
freshly ground black pepper
¹/₄ cup/45 g/1¹/₂ oz low-fat natural yogurt
³/₄ cup/185 mL/6 fl oz skim milk

1   Place flour, Parmesan and Cheddar cheeses, chives and black pepper to taste in a bowl. Stir in yogurt and milk to form a soft sticky dough.

2   Turn dough onto a lightly floured surface and knead lightly. Press dough out to a 3 cm/1¹/₄ in thickness and, using a scone cutter, cut out 5 cm/2 in rounds. Place scones on a nonstick baking tray and bake for 12-15 minutes or until scones are risen and golden.

568 kilojoules (135 Calories) per serve

Carbohydrate	23 g (68%)	high
Fat	2 g	very low

READING LABELS

▸   Ingredients on labels are listed in order of quantity, so ingredients higher on the list are present in larger amounts than ingredients lower down.

▸   Food labels cannot include any nutrition claims such as 'salt-reduced' or 'low-fat' unless a nutrition information panel is on the packaging. Compare the nutrition panels of different products to hunt out the products which contain less fat, sugar or salt (sodium).

▸   Don't be tricked by the following claims:

Cholesterol Free – food with no cholesterol may still be high in other types of fat.

Lite – lite could mean light in texture, colour or flavour. Legally it does not have to be lighter in kilojoules (calories) or fat, although it may be. Read the nutrition panel carefully.

▸   Health Food – there is no legal definition of health food. Products with these labels may still contain as much fat, sugar and salt as other products with regular labels.

▸   Compare the amount of fat and salt between products using the information per 100 g of food. In general, look for products which provide:

less than 10 g fat/100 g (or the lowest fat product by comparison)

less than 120 mg salt/100 g

Cheese and Chive Scones, Banana Muffins, Muesli Bars

Spicy Chickpeas

Serves 4
Oven temp: 180°C, 350°F, Gas 4

2 teaspoons olive oil
1/2 teaspoon chilli powder
2 teaspoons ground cumin
2 teaspoons paprika
2 teaspoons ground coriander
freshly ground black pepper
4 cups/750 g/1 1/2 lb cooked chickpeas

1   Heat oil in a small frying pan,
add chilli powder, cumin, paprika,
coriander and black pepper to taste
and cook, stirring, for 2 minutes.

2   Add spice mixture to chickpeas
and toss to combine. Spread
chickpeas over the base of a
shallow ovenproof dish and bake
for 1 hour or until crunchy. Cool and
store in an airtight container.

Cook's tip: Canned chickpeas can
be used to make this recipe. Wash
and drain chickpeas well before
using.

850 kilojoules (205 Calories) per serve

Carbohydrate	24 g (47%)	low
Fat	6 g	low

Pitta Crisps

Serves 4
Oven temp: 180°C, 350°F, Gas 4

4 pitta bread rounds, split
90 g/3 oz grated Parmesan cheese
chilli powder or dried mixed herbs

Place bread rounds on baking trays.
Sprinkle each round with Parmesan
cheese, then with chilli powder or
mixed herbs and bake for 10
minutes or until golden and crisp.
Break into pieces, allow to cool and
store in an airtight container.

Nutrition tip: These crisps are a
great low-fat alternative to potato
crisps or corn chips. Eat them on
their own or bake plain crisps and
serve with dips. For the best flavour
use fresh Parmesan cheese.

985 kilojoules (235 Calories) per serve

Carbohydrate	33 g (56%)	high
Fat	6 g	low

Honey Soy Noodles

Serves 4

4 x 85 g/3 oz packets instant noodles
(discard flavour sachet)
4 tablespoons honey
1/3 cup/90 mL/3 fl oz low-salt soy sauce
2 spring onions, finely chopped

1   Place noodles in a bowl, cover
with boiling water and set aside to
stand for 3-4 minutes.

2   Place honey, soy sauce and
spring onions in a small saucepan
and cook, stirring, over a medium
heat for 2-3 minutes or until mixture
thickens. Drain noodles, add sauce
and toss to combine.

Nutrition tip: Discard the flavouring
sachets that often come with instant
noodles. These are high in salt.

1815 kilojoules (431 Calories) per serve

Carbohydrate	95 g (87%)	very high
Fat	1 g	very low

Pitta Crisps, Spicy Chickpeas

Tuna and Corn Noodles

Serves 4

4 x 85 g/3 oz packets instant noodles
(discard flavour sachet)
¹/₂ cup/125 mL/4 fl oz tomato pasta sauce
2 x 125 g/4 oz canned sweet corn kernels,
drained
220 g/7 oz canned tuna in water, drained
and flaked

1   Place noodles in a bowl, cover
with boiling water and set aside to
stand for 3-4 minutes or until soft.

2   Place pasta sauce, sweet corn
and tuna in a small saucepan and
cook, stirring, over a medium heat
for 2-3 minutes or until heated
through. Drain noodles, add sauce
and toss to combine.

1755 kilojoules (451 Calories) per serve

Carbohydrate	73.5 g (70%)	very high
Fat	3 g	very low

SNACK RIGHT

▶   Snack, don't pick! Nibbling
little bits and pieces will feel
less satisfying, plus you have
no idea what you have eaten or
how much.

▶   Snacks are fine, even when
you are dieting. But remember
to snack carefully on the right
foods. Snack when you are
hungry – not just because
you're bored.

▶   Keep healthy snacks on
hand. Make up some of the
snack recipes in this section
and keep them for a treat. You
will then be able to grab
something quickly that is
delicious yet good for you.

▶   A pre-training snack is a
good idea, especially for
younger children, who tend to
get hungry between meals.
The right snack will boost
energy levels and performance
at training.

▶   If you can't resist crisps,
biscuits or chocolates, don't
bring them home from the
supermarket.

Honey Soy Noodles,
Tuna and Corn Noodles

Bowls and Fork Country Road

Apple Toast Turnovers

Makes 12
Oven temp: 180°C, 350°F, Gas 4

12 slices white or wholemeal bread, crusts removed
440 g/14 oz canned unsweetened pie apple or stewed apple
1/4 cup/45 g/1 1/2 oz brown sugar
1/2 teaspoon ground cinnamon
60 g/2 oz sultanas
1 tablespoon honey
1 tablespoon hot water

1   Using a rolling pin, roll bread until flat.

2   Place apple, sugar, cinnamon and sultanas in a bowl and mix to combine.

3   Place a spoonful of apple mixture in the centre of each bread slice. Bring two opposite corners together and secure with a toothpick. Place bread parcels on a nonstick baking tray.

4   Combine honey and water and mix to dissolve honey. Brush each bread parcel with honey mixture and bake for 10-15 minutes or until golden and crisp.

525 kilojoules (125 Calories) per serve
Carbohydrate   26 g (83%)   very high
Fat   1 g   very low

Apricot Toast Turnovers
Replace pie apple with 440 g/14 oz canned unsweetened pie apricots.

480 kilojoules (115 Calories) per serve
Carbohydrate   23 g (83%)   very high
Fat   1 g   very low

Pikelets

Makes 25

1 cup/125 g/4 oz self-raising flour
1 cup/155 g/5 oz wholemeal self-raising flour
1/4 cup/60 g/2 oz caster sugar
1 egg
1 1/2 cups/375 mL/12 fl oz skim milk
1 tablespoon finely grated lemon rind

1   Sift together self-raising and wholemeal self-raising flours into a bowl, return husks to bowl, add sugar and make a well in the centre of flour mixture. Combine egg, milk and lemon rind, pour into well and mix until batter is smooth.

2   Heat a nonstick frying pan over a medium heat and cook tablespoons of mixture for 1-2 minutes each side or until golden.

220 kilojoules (50 Calories) per pikelet
Carbohydrate   10 g (77%)   very high
Fat   0.5 g   very low

Blueberry Pikelets
Fold 90 g/3 oz fresh blueberries into batter before cooking.

230 kilojoules (55 Calories) per pikelet
Carbohydrate   11 g (78%)   very high
Fat   0.5 g   very low

Lemon and Currant Pikelets
Fold an extra 1/2 tablespoon finely grated lemon rind and 170 g/5 1/2 oz currants into batter before cooking.

300 kilojoules (75 Calories) per pikelet
Carbohydrate   15 g (82%)   very high
Fat   0.5 g   very low

Quick Banana Rice Custard

Serves 4

1 cup/220 g/7 oz short-grain rice
3 cups/750 mL/1 1/4 pt water
2 cups/500 mL/16 fl oz reduced-fat milk
2 tablespoons custard powder blended with 2 tablespoons water
2 tablespoons sugar
2 bananas, chopped
ground cinnamon

1   Place rice, water and milk in a saucepan and bring to the boil. Reduce heat and simmer, stirring occasionally, for 12-15 minutes or until rice is tender.

2   Stir in custard powder mixture and sugar and cook for 2-3 minutes longer. Add banana and mix to combine. Spoon rice into serving bowls and sprinkle with cinnamon.

Microwave it: Place rice, water and milk in a large microwave-safe container and cook on HIGH (100%) for 10-12 minutes or until rice is tender. Stir in custard powder mixture and sugar and cook for 1-2 minutes longer. Add banana and mix to combine.

1400 kilojoules (335 Calories) per serve
Carbohydrate   73 g (86%)   very high
Fat   0.5 g   very low

Right: Pikelets, Apple Toast Turnovers
Below: Quick Banana Rice Custard

TOPPING UP

Snack on carbohydrate foods to help you top up your energy levels. Try some of the following:

▶   Bread or toast, including raisin bread, crumpets, English muffins.

▶   Breakfast cereal with reduced-fat milk or low-fat yogurt, topped with fruit.

▶   Creamed rice – leftover rice mixed with reduced-fat milk or low-fat yogurt.

▶   Fresh, canned or dried fruit.

▶   Drink your snack. See page 33 for delicious drink ideas.

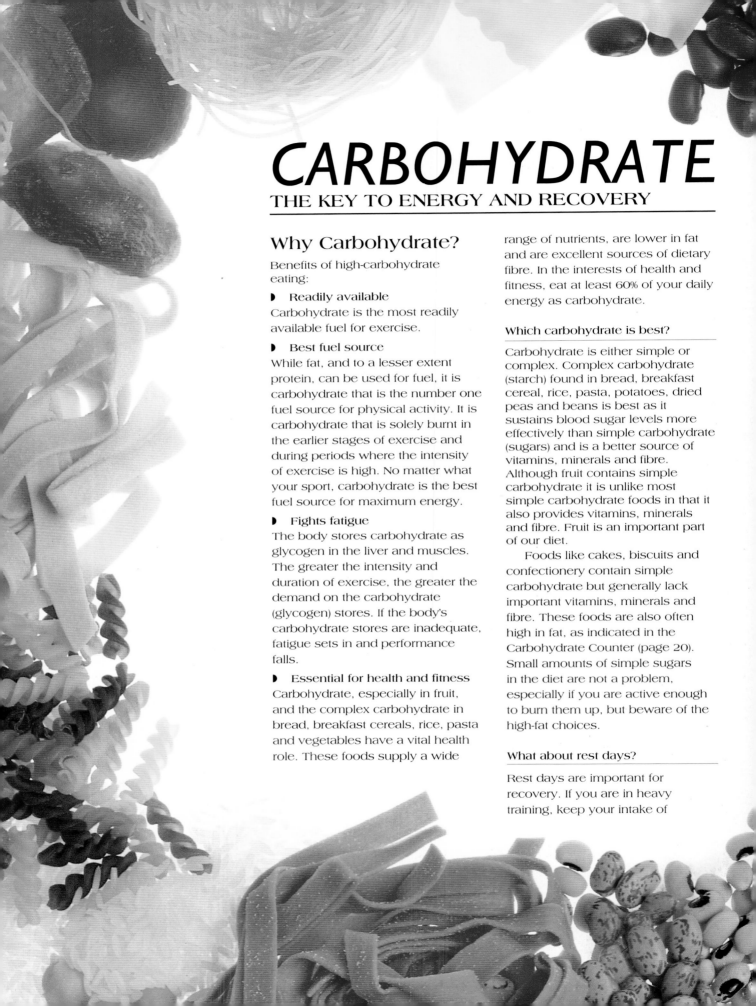

CARBOHYDRATE
THE KEY TO ENERGY AND RECOVERY

Why Carbohydrate?

Benefits of high-carbohydrate eating:

▶ **Readily available**
Carbohydrate is the most readily available fuel for exercise.

▶ **Best fuel source**
While fat, and to a lesser extent protein, can be used for fuel, it is carbohydrate that is the number one fuel source for physical activity. It is carbohydrate that is solely burnt in the earlier stages of exercise and during periods where the intensity of exercise is high. No matter what your sport, carbohydrate is the best fuel source for maximum energy.

▶ **Fights fatigue**
The body stores carbohydrate as glycogen in the liver and muscles. The greater the intensity and duration of exercise, the greater the demand on the carbohydrate (glycogen) stores. If the body's carbohydrate stores are inadequate, fatigue sets in and performance falls.

▶ **Essential for health and fitness**
Carbohydrate, especially in fruit, and the complex carbohydrate in bread, breakfast cereals, rice, pasta and vegetables have a vital health role. These foods supply a wide range of nutrients, are lower in fat and are excellent sources of dietary fibre. In the interests of health and fitness, eat at least 60% of your daily energy as carbohydrate.

Which carbohydrate is best?

Carbohydrate is either simple or complex. Complex carbohydrate (starch) found in bread, breakfast cereal, rice, pasta, potatoes, dried peas and beans is best as it sustains blood sugar levels more effectively than simple carbohydrate (sugars) and is a better source of vitamins, minerals and fibre. Although fruit contains simple carbohydrate it is unlike most simple carbohydrate foods in that it also provides vitamins, minerals and fibre. Fruit is an important part of our diet.

Foods like cakes, biscuits and confectionery contain simple carbohydrate but generally lack important vitamins, minerals and fibre. These foods are also often high in fat, as indicated in the Carbohydrate Counter (page 20). Small amounts of simple sugars in the diet are not a problem, especially if you are active enough to burn them up, but beware of the high-fat choices.

What about rest days?

Rest days are important for recovery. If you are in heavy training, keep your intake of carbohydrate up to the recommended amount for training days – the unused carbohydrate will be stored in the muscles and liver and will help to ensure that your body is recharged for your next training session!

Your carbohydrate needs

To estimate the amount of carbohydrate you require, multiply your weight by the suitable amount of carbohydrate shown in the table.

For example, if your activity level is moderate and you weigh 70 kg:

70 kg x 6-7 g carbohydrate/kg = 420-490 g of carbohydrate per day

Use the Carbohydrate Counter (page 20) to work out how much bread, fruit, pasta, rice, potato, cereal or other carbohydrate foods you will need to eat each day.

HOW MUCH CARBOHYDRATE?

The amount of carbohydrate you require depends on your weight and activity level. Use the following guide to work out how much you need each day.

Activity level*	Grams of carbohydrate/kg body weight/day
Light (less than 1 hour/day)	4-5
Light-moderate (1 hour/day)	5-6
Moderate (1-2 hours/day)	6-7
Moderate-heavy (2-4 hours/day)	7-8
Heavy (more than 4 hours/day)	8-10

* Note: Activity levels refer to the intensity as well as the duration of the activity. The time refers to the amount of time you are physically active during training, not the amount of time at training.

CARBOHYDRATE COUNTER

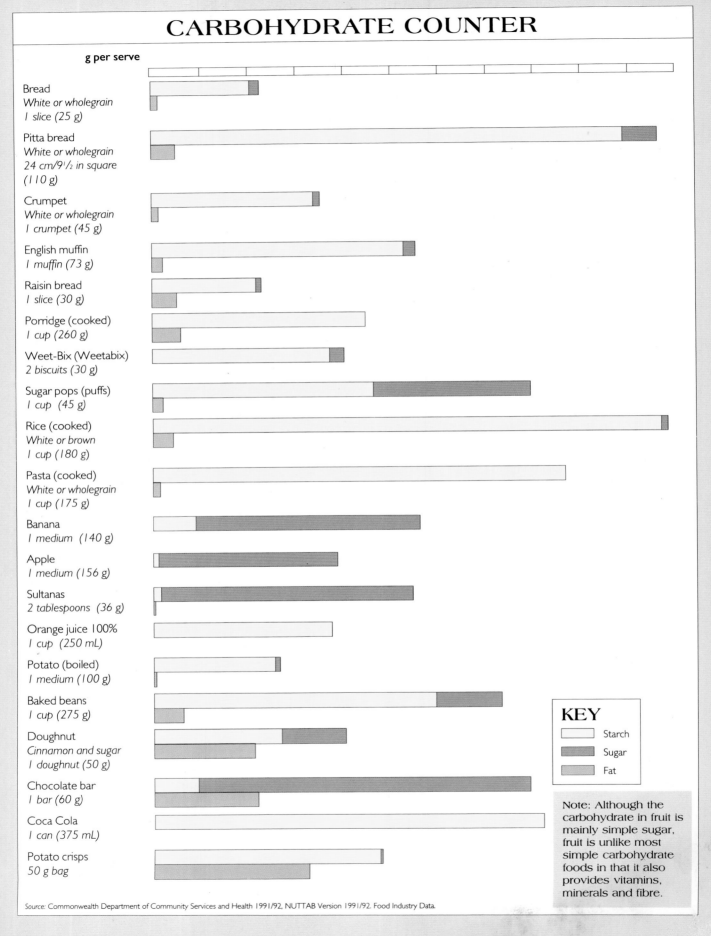

g per serve

Bread
White or wholegrain
1 slice (25 g)

Pitta bread
White or wholegrain
24 cm/9½ in square
(110 g)

Crumpet
White or wholegrain
1 crumpet (45 g)

English muffin
1 muffin (73 g)

Raisin bread
1 slice (30 g)

Porridge (cooked)
1 cup (260 g)

Weet-Bix (Weetabix)
2 biscuits (30 g)

Sugar pops (puffs)
1 cup (45 g)

Rice (cooked)
White or brown
1 cup (180 g)

Pasta (cooked)
White or wholegrain
1 cup (175 g)

Banana
1 medium (140 g)

Apple
1 medium (156 g)

Sultanas
2 tablespoons (36 g)

Orange juice 100%
1 cup (250 mL)

Potato (boiled)
1 medium (100 g)

Baked beans
1 cup (275 g)

Doughnut
Cinnamon and sugar
1 doughnut (50 g)

Chocolate bar
1 bar (60 g)

Coca Cola
1 can (375 mL)

Potato crisps
50 g bag

KEY

☐ Starch
▨ Sugar
▨ Fat

Note: Although the carbohydrate in fruit is mainly simple sugar, fruit is unlike most simple carbohydrate foods in that it also provides vitamins, minerals and fibre.

Source: Commonwealth Department of Community Services and Health 1991/92, NUTTAB Version 1991/92. Food Industry Data.

Carbohydrate and Recovery

After exercise, the muscles are hungry for carbohydrate. If carbohydrate intake is delayed, the muscles are starved of what they need most. Many sportspeople fail to feed their muscles soon enough after exercise. Instead, they take a shower, chat to their team mates and delay eating until they get home, usually more than an hour after training.

Eating or drinking carbohydrate immediately (within 15 minutes) after strenuous aerobic-based exercise has been shown to enhance recovery by speeding up glycogen replacement. If you train hard each day, it is essential that you refuel your muscles promptly – there's no time to waste.

Most people find high-carbohydrate drinks easier to consume, as they are usually more thirsty than hungry after training or competition. A drink is generally more convenient than food and aids rehydration as well. Recovery will be incomplete if the body remains dehydrated (page 34).

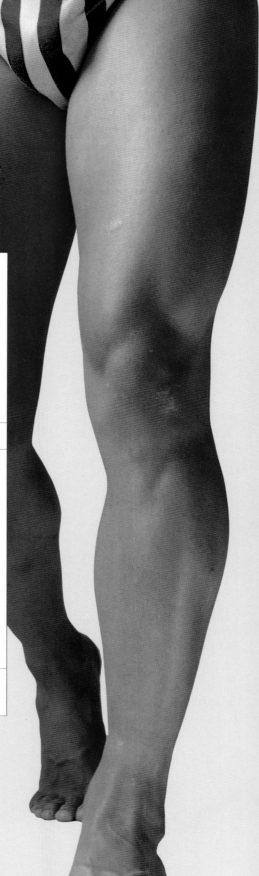

EAT AND DRINK TO RECOVERY

Aim to consume approximately 1 g of carbohydrate/kg of body weight in the first two hours after exercise. In practical terms, this amounts to consuming around 50-100 g (more if your lean weight is over 100 kg) of carbohydrate every two hours until you are able to eat a high-carbohydrate meal.

The following list of 50 g carbohydrate options will give you a few ideas of what to eat and drink. Remember you must also drink plenty of fluid to rehydrate.

Drinks

▶ 250 mL/8 fl oz high-carbohydrate sports drink such as Exceed High Carbohydrate Source

▶ 250-300 mL/8-9½ fl oz liquid meal such as Exceed Sports Nutrition Supplement or Sustagen

▶ 500-1000 mL/16 fl oz-1¾ pt fluid-replacement drink (5-10% carbohydrate)

▶ 750 mL/1¼ pt cordial or 500 mL/16 fl oz soft drink, juice* or flavoured mineral water

Food

▶ 1-1½ jam or honey sandwiches

▶ 1 banana* sandwich

▶ 1 muffin (page 13)

▶ 1 Lebanese bread (24 cm/9½ in square)

▶ 2 medium-large bananas*

▶ 4 tablespoons sultanas*

▶ 2 Muesli Bars (page 13)

▶ 1 Exceed Sports bar

*Fructose sugar in fruit and juice does not seem to be as effective in replacing muscle glycogen stores as glucose.

LUNCHES
FOR PEAK PERFORMANCE

Citrus and Nectarine Salad

Serves 4

1 lettuce, leaves separated and torn into pieces
2 oranges, segmented
250 g/8 oz cherry tomatoes, halved
6 nectarines, stoned and quartered
1 red pepper, cut into strips
4 slices reduced-fat-and-salt ham, cut into strips

CITRUS DRESSING
1 tablespoon lemon juice
2 tablespoons orange juice
2 teaspoons sugar

1 Arrange lettuce, oranges, tomatoes, nectarines, red pepper and ham in a salad bowl.

2 To make dressing, place lemon juice, orange juice and sugar in a screwtop jar and shake to combine. Drizzle over salad and serve immediately.

Lunchbox tip: Place salad into a container and take dressing in a small jar. Just prior to serving, drizzle dressing over salad.

518 kilojoules (125 Calories) per serve
Carbohydrate   20 g (63%)   high
Fat   1 g   very low

Chicken Salad with Herb Mayonnaise

Serves 4

2 boneless chicken breast fillets
mixed lettuce leaves
60 g/2 oz snow pea sprouts or watercress
2 carrots, cut into strips
2 zucchini (courgettes) cut into strips
1 tomato, chopped

HERB DRESSING
4 tablespoons low-oil mayonnaise
3 tablespoons chopped fresh herbs of your choice

1 Heat a nonstick frying pan over a medium heat, add chicken and cook for 2-3 minutes each side or until cooked through. Remove chicken from pan and set aside to cool.

2 Cut chicken into strips. Arrange lettuce, snow pea sprouts or watercress, carrots, zucchini (courgettes) and tomato in a salad bowl.

3 To make dressing, combine mayonnaise and herbs and spoon over salad.

365 kilojoules (90 Calories) per serve
Carbohydrate   4 g (17%)   low
Fat   2 g   very low

Spinach and Pasta Salad

Serves 4

500 g/1 lb pasta of your choice
4 spring onions, finely chopped
8-10 stalks English spinach, chopped
2 tomatoes, chopped
155 g/5 oz reduced-fat feta cheese, chopped
12 button mushrooms sliced
1 red pepper, chopped

CHILLI DRESSING
2 tablespoons red wine vinegar
1 tablespoon sweet chilli sauce
1/4 cup/60 mL/2 fl oz no-oil French dressing

1 Cook pasta in boiling water in a large saucepan following packet directions. Drain, rinse under cold running water, then drain again and set aside to cool completely.

2 Place pasta, spring onions, spinach, tomatoes, feta cheese, mushrooms and red pepper in a salad bowl.

3 To make dressing, place vinegar, chilli sauce and French dressing in a screwtop jar and shake well to combine. Spoon dressing over salad and toss to combine.

2260 kilojoules (540 Calories) per serve
Carbohydrate   82 g (61%)   high
Fat   8 g   low

Chicken Salad with Herb Mayonnaise, Spinach and Pasta Salad, Citrus and Nectarine Salad

Green Bowl Country Road   Blue Bowls Orrefors Kosta Boda   Rackets and Balls Rebel Sports

Salmon Bread Quiche

Serves 4
Oven temp: 180°C, 350°F, Gas 4

7 thick slices white or wholemeal bread, toasted and crusts removed

SALMON FILLING
4 eggs, lightly beaten
1¼ cups/375 mL/12 fl oz reduced-fat milk
185 g/6 oz canned salmon in water, drained and flaked
1 tablespoon chopped fresh herbs of your choice
60 g/2 oz grated reduced-fat Cheddar cheese
freshly ground black pepper

1   Line a 23 cm/9 in square ovenproof dish with nonstick baking paper then with toast, cutting toast to fit.

2   To make filling, place eggs, milk, salmon, herbs, cheese and black pepper to taste in a bowl and mix to combine.

3   Pour filling into dish and bake for 25-30 minutes or until set and golden. Serve hot, warm or cold with salad.

1460 kilojoules (345 Calories) per serve
Carbohydrate   26 g (29%)   low
Fat   15 g   medium

Turkey Bakes

Serves 2
Oven temp: 180°C, 350°F, Gas 4

4 slices wholegrain bread
2 tablespoons low-oil mayonnaise
1 small tomato, sliced
4 slices reduced-fat cooked turkey, cut into strips
2 tablespoons cranberry sauce
1 small red pepper, sliced
60 g/2 oz grated reduced-fat Swiss cheese

1   Spread bread with mayonnaise.

2   Top each slice of bread with tomato, turkey, cranberry sauce and red pepper then sprinkle with cheese.

3   Place on a nonstick baking tray and bake for 10-15 minutes or until crunchy and golden.

1160 kilojoules (275 Calories) per serve
Carbohydrate   28 g (39%)   low
Fat   8 g   low

Ham and Pineapple Bakes

Serves 2
Oven temp: 180°C, 350°F, Gas 4

4 slices wholemeal bread
2 tablespoons low-oil mayonnaise
4 slices reduced-fat-and-salt ham, cut into thick strips
1 small green pepper, chopped
8 button mushrooms, sliced
220 g/7 oz canned unsweetened pineapple pieces, drained
60 g/2 oz grated reduced-fat Cheddar cheese

1   Spread bread with mayonnaise.

2   Top each slice of bread with ham, green pepper, mushrooms and pineapple, then sprinkle with cheese.

3   Place on a nonstick baking tray and bake for 10-15 minutes or until crunchy and golden.

1415 kilojoules (335 Calories) per serve
Carbohydrate   37 g (43%)   low
Fat   9.5 g   low

Sandwiches with delicious and healthy fillings, Ham and Pineapple Melts, Turkey Melts, Salmon Bread Quiche

Delicious Sandwich Fillings

Avoid spreading bread with butter or margarine. Instead, try the following: no-oil mayonnaise, chutney, mustard, small amount of avocado, hummus.

▶ Snow pea sprouts or watercress, 10 g/¼ oz pâté and tomato

▶ Cottage cheese, ¼ avocado, tomato, lettuce and chilli sauce

▶ Fruit bread with banana, sultanas and cinnamon

▶ Lettuce, 45 g/1½ oz salmon, no-oil mayonnaise, gherkins and grated carrot

▶ Lettuce, 1 hard-boiled egg, low-oil mayonnaise mixed with curry powder

▶ Red pepper, 45 g/1½ oz drained canned tuna in water, pickles, lettuce and bean sprouts

▶ Hummus, tabbouleh and 1 slice reduced-fat Cheddar cheese

▶ Lean lamb, mint jelly and salad

▶ Lean rare roast beef, wholegrain mustard, lettuce, tomato and cucumber

BASICALLY BREAD

Bread is a nutritious food that we can all enjoy. Health experts agree that we should all be eating more of it.

▶ Bread is not fattening; in fact, it is low in fat and sugar and contains significant quantities of protein, vitamins (especially thiamin), minerals, complex carbohydrate and dietary fibre.

▶ For interest, use a variety of breads.

▶ For a more filling sandwich, make a double-decker sandwich using three slices of bread instead of two. Why not try using different varieties of bread in the one sandwich; for example, use one slice of white and two slices of wholegrain or wholemeal.

▶ Bread keeps well in the freezer and if you like to eat a variety of breads this is a good way to store them. It is easy to remove just one or two slices and bread thaws quickly at room temperature or in the microwave.

▶ Freezing does not affect the nutritional value of bread.

Plates Limoges

Chicken Satay Roll-Ups

Serves 2

2 pitta bread rounds
2 lettuce leaves, shredded
1 small tomato, sliced
1 small green pepper, sliced
60 g/2 oz chopped cooked chicken

SATAY SAUCE
1 tablespoon peanut butter
¼ teaspoon ground cumin
2 tablespoons low-oil mayonnaise
1 teaspoon low-salt soy sauce

1   To make sauce, place peanut butter, cumin, mayonnaise and soy sauce in a small bowl and mix to combine.

2   Top bread rounds with lettuce, tomato, green pepper and chicken. Spoon over sauce and roll up.

1165 kilojoules (395 Calories) per serve
Carbohydrate	53 g (53%)	medium
Fat	10 g	medium

Tuna Salad with Curry Mayonnaise

Serves 4

200 g/6½ oz broccoli, broken into florets
100 g/3½ oz snow peas (mangetout)
mixed lettuce leaves
2 cups/440 g/14 oz rice, cooked
440 g/14 oz canned tuna in water, drained and flaked
1 red pepper, chopped
1 yellow or green pepper, chopped
2 carrots, chopped

CURRY DRESSING
½ cup/125 mL/4 fl oz low-oil mayonnaise
2 teaspoons curry powder

1   Boil, steam or microwave broccoli and snow peas (mangetout) separately until just tender. Drain and refresh under cold running water.

2   Line a salad bowl with lettuce leaves. Combine rice, tuna, red pepper, yellow or green pepper, carrots, broccoli and snow peas (mangetout) and arrange on lettuce leaves.

3   To make dressing, place mayonnaise and curry powder in a bowl and mix to combine. Drizzle dressing over salad. Serve immediately or cover and chill.

1535 kilojoules (365 Calories) per serve
Carbohydrate	49 g (52%)	medium
Fat	4.5 g	very low

Spicy Salad Pockets

Serves 2

2 small pocket bread rounds

SALAD FILLING
6 curly endive or lettuce leaves
1 tomato, sliced
1 small cucumber, sliced
15 g/½ oz snow pea sprouts or watercress
1 small carrot, grated
45 g/1½ oz grated reduced-fat Cheddar cheese

SPICY DRESSING

¹/₄ cup/60 mL/2 fl oz low-oil mayonnaise
2 teaspoons chilli sauce
2 teaspoons chopped fresh coriander

1   To make dressing, place mayonnaise, chilli sauce and coriander in a small bowl and mix to combine.

2   Make a small slit in the side of each bread round and fill with endive or lettuce, tomato, cucumber, snow pea sprouts or watercress, carrot and cheese. Drizzle with a little mayonnaise.

Cook's tip: The Spicy Dressing will keep in the refrigerator for several days and is delicious used as a dressing for your favourite salad or sandwiches.

980 kilojoules (235 Calories) per serve

Carbohydrate	*31 g (43%)*	*low*
Fat	*6 g*	*low*

Perfect Potato Salad

Serves 4

1 kg/2 lb baby new potatoes
2 leeks, finely sliced

FRESH HERB DRESSING
¹/₂ cup/125 mL/4 fl oz low-oil mayonnaise
¹/₄ cup/45 g/1¹/₂ oz low-fat natural yogurt
2 tablespoons snipped fresh chives
1 tablespoon chopped fresh dill
freshly ground black pepper

1   Bring a large saucepan of water to the boil, add potatoes and boil for 6-8 minutes or until tender. Drain potatoes and set aside to cool.

2   Place leeks in a nonstick frying pan and cook over a medium heat for 3-4 minutes or until golden. Cut potatoes in half and place in a bowl, add leeks and toss to combine.

3   To make dressing, place mayonnaise, yogurt, chives, dill and black pepper to taste in a bowl and mix to combine. Spoon dressing over salad and toss to combine. Chill well before serving.

670 kilojoules (160 Calories) per serve

Carbohydrate	*31 g (79%)*	*very high*
Fat	*0.5 g*	*very low*

Left: Chicken Satay Roll-Ups, Spicy Salad Pockets
Top right: Tuna Salad with Curry Mayonnaise
Right: Perfect Potato Salad

BULKING UP
HOW TO BUILD BETTER BICEPS

Muscle-building pills and potions make a lot more money than muscle! The following Bulking-Up Brief gives you the scientific facts that could save you a lot of wasted time, effort and money.

BULKING-UP BRIEF

This will help you to build better biceps. Go for it!

Step 1

Training

▶ Obtain a professionally planned weight-training program.

▶ Aerobic training may need to be reduced (this will leave more fuel available for muscle growth).

▶ Make use of the 'off season' – it's easier to devote more attention to weight training then.

Step 2

Increase energy (kilojoule/calorie) intake

▶ Don't skip meals.

▶ Snack between meals (see page 13 for snack ideas). Remember if you are too full to eat, try a liquid meal instead (page 33).

▶ Drink high-energy drinks e.g. sports drinks – especially high-carbohydrate and milk-based sports drinks, reduced-fat milk and juices, instead of water, tea or coffee.

▶ If feeling too full is a problem, reduce your fibre intake. For example replace some wholegrain foods with more refined foods. Eat white bread, and cereals such as Cornflakes, Rice Bubbles (Crispies) and Special K instead of wholegrain bread and high-fibre cereals.

▶ Get organised. Prepare some meals and snacks ahead of time and keep them close by so there's less chance you'll skip them.

Step 3

Balancing protein, fat and carbohydrate

▶ Don't binge on protein, but do include a protein choice at each meal.

▶ Remember, protein intake will naturally increase to a sufficient level once you're eating more food.

▶ Carbohydrate provides energy – the body will use muscle protein for fuel if your carbohydrate intake is too low.

▶ Keep fat intake low to prevent gains in body fat.

Step 4

Monitoring progress

▶ Expect gains in the range of up to 0.5 kg/1 lb a week.

▶ Remember that rapid gains include undesirable body fat.

▶ If possible, monitor body fat with a skinfold (pinch) test (see page 74).

▶ Be patient – gaining muscle takes time.

Athletes refer to muscle gain as 'bulking up'. Athletes may want to bulk up:

▶ to increase strength for sports performance;

▶ to protect against injury – especially in body contact sports such as football;

▶ to improve physique – just to look and feel better.

It would seem to most people entering a weight-training gym that the secret to 'bulking up' lies in one of the umpteen supplements or containers of weight gain powder. Supplementation is advertised widely and promoted heavily by the anecdotes of 'Mr Universe' athletes. Their testimonials are supported financially, but not scientifically! The secret of success lies in the correct combination of diet and weight training. Weight training stimulates muscle growth, the diet provides the nutrients needed for growth and the fuel necessary for training.

As muscle is made of protein, athletes often think that a massive protein intake is necessary for massive muscle growth. The facts are that the body can only use a limited amount of protein each day. The excess is treated as waste and is excreted in the urine. This excess protein places an extra, unnecessary load on the kidneys. If the protein foods chosen contain fat or cholesterol (e.g. eggs, meat, full-cream milk) then the diet will also be high in fat. Research studies have found high levels of cholesterol in the blood of athletes following these high-protein diets. Use of anabolic steroids for muscle bulking, contributes to elevated cholesterol levels and further increases the risk for heart disease.

'Why do I have difficulty gaining muscle bulk?'

Physical activity burns up energy. If your food intake is insufficient then the body uses its stores of energy in the form of fat and muscle to keep it going. Young males in particular have high energy requirements; strenuous training increases their needs even further.

Often these requirements are more than the appetite allows, so it becomes difficult to consume the amount of food fuel needed to replace what is used up, let alone eat the extra amount necessary to fuel muscle growth. Frequently, strenuous training and busy work schedules take up valuable eating time. Some athletes also feel uncomfortable eating a snack prior to exercise and may not feel hungry until several hours after training.

If you are having difficulty bulking up use the Bulking-Up Brief on page 28 to help you get on the right track.

Body-Builder Drinks

Liquid supplements are useful in that they are quick, easy and tend not to fill you up too much. They are therefore an easy way to get extra energy (kilojoules/calories). The body-builder varieties tend to place too much emphasis on protein. Your own homemade drinks (see page 33) are better balanced and will be substantially cheaper. Commercially available liquid meals such as Exceed Sports Nutrition Supplement and Sustagen are suitable if you don't want to make your own.

Men naturally have greater muscular development than women due to higher levels of the hormone testosterone.

Amino Acid Supplements

The claims for amino acid supplements are growing, mainly as the result of clever marketing. 'Aminos' have been around for some time; however, there is really no substantial scientific support for their use. Amino acids are the building blocks of protein. Protein-rich foods are a much better source of amino acids than amino acid supplements. Claims that specific amino acid preparations stimulate growth hormone, have not been supported by scientific research.

Amino acid companies do not provide a money-back guarantee if amino acids don't work. Companies which sell pharmaceuticals are obligated to demonstrate the efficacy and safety of any product prior to it being approved for sale. As consumers, we would not expect any less. Yet when it comes to amino acids and countless other nutrition supplements, many people are willing to accept the advertising blurb as scientific proof.

AMINO ACID COMPARISONS
Amino acid supplements versus food

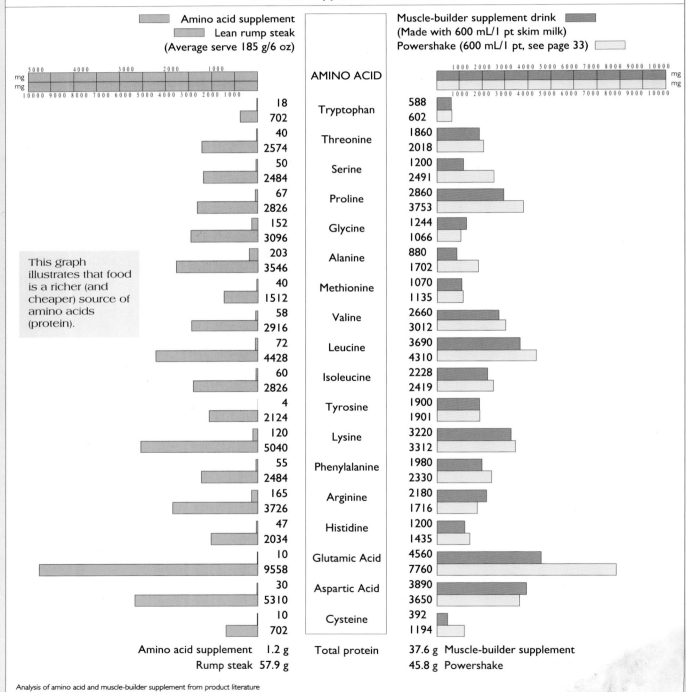

This graph illustrates that food is a richer (and cheaper) source of amino acids (protein).

	Amino acid supplement	Lean rump steak (Average serve 185 g/6 oz)	AMINO ACID	Muscle-builder supplement drink (Made with 600 mL/1 pt skim milk)	Powershake (600 mL/1 pt, see page 33)
	18	702	Tryptophan	588	602
	40	2574	Threonine	1860	2018
	50	2484	Serine	1200	2491
	67	2826	Proline	2860	3753
	152	3096	Glycine	1244	1066
	203	3546	Alanine	880	1702
	40	1512	Methionine	1070	1135
	58	2916	Valine	2660	3012
	72	4428	Leucine	3690	4310
	60	2826	Isoleucine	2228	2419
	4	2124	Tyrosine	1900	1901
	120	5040	Lysine	3220	3312
	55	2484	Phenylalanine	1980	2330
	165	3726	Arginine	2180	1716
	47	2034	Histidine	1200	1435
	10	9558	Glutamic Acid	4560	7760
	30	5310	Aspartic Acid	3890	3650
	10	702	Cysteine	392	1194

Amino acid supplement 1.2 g
Rump steak 57.9 g

Total protein

37.6 g Muscle-builder supplement
45.8 g Powershake

Analysis of amino acid and muscle-builder supplement from product literature
Source: McCance and Widdowson's 'The Composition of Foods' (First Supplement) by A.A. Paul, D.A.T. Southgate and J. Russell.

TEN DIETARY MISTAKES MADE BY ATHLETES

1 Skipping meals

Training can be very time consuming. Often meals are skipped when time just runs out. Unfortunately, this can mean that energy reserves also run out – just like a car running out of petrol. Use this book to help you organise food which is fast and healthy so you can quickly and easily refuel your body at each meal.

2 Not enough carbohydrate

Foods rich in carbohydrate – particularly complex carbohydrate – need to become the major food group that you eat at each meal. One big bowl of pasta in the evening is not enough. Include a variety of carbohydrate foods such as bread, cereal, rice, pasta, potatoes, fruit and juice at each meal. The table on page 19 will help you work out your carbohydrate needs.

3 Too much fat

One of the reasons why we may not eat enough carbohydrate is that we fill up on fat. The fat we eat is all too easily converted to body fat and cholesterol – leading to a higher prevalence of obesity and heart disease when fat intake is too high.

Some people who are lean and fit become blasé about eating fat. While they may be lean and have no cholesterol problems, diseases like gall stones and certain cancers (especially those of the breast and bowel) are also linked with eating too much fat.

If their high-fat diet continues and exercise doesn't, they'll end up wearing more fat than they burn off!

4 Too much salt

Even if you train hard and sweat a lot, your diet will provide adequate salt – there's no need to add any extra salt to your food. As you get fitter, you will sweat more during exercise, this is because your body becomes better equipped to keep itself cool. The body manages to conserve salt by reducing the concentration of the salt in sweat (and urine). So the more you sweat, the less salty it gets.

5 Supplement addiction – are you hooked?

Athletic people often feel that they can't get by without supplements. They may do nothing about their food intake, thinking that supplements can make up for what they might be missing out on. The truth is that vitamin and mineral supplements do not make up for too little carbohydrate or too much fat. The only way to be well nourished is to eat well. Supplements have not been shown to improve athletic performance in well-nourished people. Large doses of vitamins and minerals can be toxic and may interfere with normal nutrient absorption. Nutrition supplements do have a role to play in some situations, see Vitamins and Minerals (page 77).

6 Don't rely on your thirst

Fluid intake should be adequate to replace what is lost as sweat. Your thirst is not a good indicator of how much fluid you need – by the time you feel thirsty, you are already dehydrated. Dehydration decreases athletic performance – it's also dangerous. See page 34 for more information.

7 Fibre – too much of a good thing?

Fibre is nature's natural appetite suppressant, it helps you to feel full and to moderate your intake. It also exercises your bowel and helps to keep you regular. Too much fibre, however, is not a good thing. For a start, you will feel bloated and won't be able to get through the day without numerous trips to the bathroom.

Active people who exercise regularly and include liberal amounts of wholegrains, vegetables and fruit in their diet do not need unprocessed bran or fibre supplements. In fact, they may need to substitute wholegrains with some 'white' varieties of bread, cereal, rice or pasta. They may be getting more fibre than their bowel can handle. Fibre is a good thing, but don't go overboard.

8 Dieting – on the edge

Most of us are not perfectly happy with our shape. Generally, it's the body fat which frustrates us the most, perhaps to the point of desperation. It's at this stage that we are more susceptible to fad diets and their promises of quick and easy weight loss.

Sometimes even sensible dieting can get out of hand. For example, low-fat turns into no-fat, and little by little the amount of food eaten dwindles to almost nothing. Energy levels slide, yet weight may not budge. Dieting 'on the edge' is dangerous, ineffective in the long term and will leave its mark both physically and psychologically. For safe, sensible and successful approaches see page 74.

9 Being too pure

We've all met at least one; the person who controls every urge to sneak a morsel of fat, sugar or salt. They never put a tooth near a chocolate bar, cake or ice cream. While their dedication to perfect eating is admirable, it's not optimal and it's certainly anti-social.

Being sensible about your diet means you can splurge now and then. This helps to keep you in balance socially and mentally. We all need to relax a little sometimes so we can enjoy the full benefits of training and life.

10 Comparing intakes

The amount of food needed varies widely between people. Even if age, sex, height, weight and physical activity are taken into account, there are still individual factors. Some lucky people therefore just need to eat more than others. If you constantly compare yourself to others you may get frustrated and lose focus of what is right for you.

Glasses Home and Garden on the Mall and Country Road

DRINKS
ENERGY IN A GLASS

Chocolate Milkshake

Serves 1

1 cup/250 mL/8 fl oz reduced-fat milk
2 tablespoons low-fat vanilla yogurt
1 tablespoon skim milk powder
2 tablespoons chocolate topping (sauce) or
2 tablespoons chocolate drink powder

Place milk, yogurt, milk powder and chocolate topping or chocolate drink powder in a food processor or blender and process until thick and frothy. Pour into a serving glass and serve immediately.

1260 kilojoules (400 Calories) per serve
Carbohydrate   50 g (63%)   high
Fat   4.5 g   very low

Caramel Milkshake
Replace chocolate topping (sauce) with 2 tablespoons caramel topping (sauce).

1195 kilojoules (285 Calories) per serve
Carbohydrate   45 g (62%)   high
Fat   5 g   low

Vanilla Milkshake
Replace chocolate topping (sauce) with 1 teaspoon vanilla essence.

850 kilojoules (200 Calories) per serve
Carbohydrate   25 g (47%)   low
Fat   4.5 g   very low

Strawberry Milkshake
Replace chocolate topping (sauce) with 8 fresh strawberries or 2 tablespoons strawberry topping (sauce).

1195 kilojoules (285 Calories) per serve
Carbohydrate   46 g (62%)   high
Fat   4.5 g   very low

Mango Smoothie

Serves 1

1 cup/250 mL/8 fl oz reduced-fat milk
1/4 cup low-fat vanilla yogurt
1 tablespoon skim milk powder
2 teaspoons honey (optional)
4 ice cubes
1/2 mango, stoned, peeled and chopped

Place milk, yogurt, milk powder, honey (if using), ice cubes and mango in a food processor or blender and process until smooth. Pour into a serving glass and serve immediately.

1240 kilojoules (295 Calories) per serve
Carbohydrate   47 g (61%)   high
Fat   5 g   low

Banana Smoothie
Replace mango with 1 banana.

1570 kilojoules (375 Calories) per serve
Carbohydrate   65 g (67%)   high
Fat   5 g   low

Peach and Apricot Smoothie
Replace mango with 1 peeled and sliced peach and 2 chopped apricots.

1425 kilojoules (340 Calories) per serve
Carbohydrate   55 g (63%)   high
Fat   5 g   low

Watermelon Crush

Serves 1

10 ice cubes
1 tablespoon lemon juice
500 g/1 lb chopped watermelon

Place ice cubes, lemon juice and watermelon in a food processor or blender and process until smooth. Pour into a serving glass and serve immediately.

485 kilojoules (115 Calories) per serve
Carbohydrate   25 g (86%)   very high
Fat   1 g   very low

Melon Crush
Replace watermelon with 500 g/1 lb chopped rockmelon (cantaloupe) and honeydew melon.

464 kilojoules (110 Calories) per serve
Carbohydrate   24 g (86%)   very high
Fat   0.5 g   very low

Pineapple Crush
Replace watermelon with 500 g/1 lb chopped pineapple and 1 tablespoon chopped fresh mint.

1535 kilojoules (365 Calories) per serve
Carbohydrate   84 g (93%)   very high
Fat   0 g   nil

Mixed Fruit Crush
Replace watermelon with 1 chopped orange, 1 chopped banana and 1 chopped kiwifruit.

855 kilojoules (205 Calories) per serve
Carbohydrate   45.5 g (88%)   very high
Fat   0.5 g   very low

Powershake

Serves 1

1 cup/250 mL/8 fl oz reduced-fat milk
3 tablespoons low-fat vanilla yogurt
2 tablespoons skim milk powder
2 tablespoons unprocessed bran
1 tablespoon wheat germ
2 teaspoons honey
1 banana, chopped
4 ice cubes

Place milk, yogurt, milk powder, bran, wheat germ, honey, banana and ice cubes in a food processor or blender and process until smooth. Pour into a serving glass and serve immediately.

1900 kilojoules (450 Calories) per serve
Carbohydrate   74 g (63%)   high
Fat   6 g   low

FIBRE

Reasons for choosing a high-fibre diet.

▶ Fibre, especially the fibre found in breads and cereals, promotes normal bowel action and prevents constipation.

▶ Blood cholesterol levels may be reduced by the soluble fibre found in fruits and vegetables, particularly the legumes, as well as rice, barley and oats.

▶ Fibre promotes fullness. High-fibre foods help to satisfy the appetite and prevent overeating.

▶ There is evidence to suggest that a high-fibre intake reduces the risk of bowel cancer.

Watermelon Crush, Strawberry Milkshake, Pineapple Crush, Mango Smoothie, Mixed Fruit Crush, Chocolate Milkshake

KEEP COOL
WHEN THE HEAT'S ON

Sweating helps you keep cool during exercise, just like the radiator of a car keeps the engine cool. When there's not enough water in the radiator, the car overheats – just as you do when you're dehydrated.

Overheating or heat stress during exercise decreases performance. Severe heat stress is dangerous. Permanent physical damage, even death, can eventuate if fluid intake is neglected. Even the fittest athletes can get caught out.

'How much fluid do I need to drink?'

Fluid requirements for exercise differ according to the amount of sweat lost. The most accurate way of working out your fluid requirements is by measuring your pre- and post-exercise weight. Your body is about 60% water and each 1 litre/1¾ pt of water weighs about 1 kg/2 lb. The amount of weight you lose during exercise corresponds to the amount of water lost as sweat. Water losses greater than 2% of body weight are detrimental to performance; losses of 5% or more are extremely dangerous. Aim to keep your losses under 2% by replacing fluids as you go. A 70 kg/11 stone person should aim to keep fluid loss during an event to less than 2% of 70 kg/11 stone, which is about 1.4 kg/3 lb.

Top up – don't guzzle

Don't wait until you are thirsty to start drinking. During exercise, your thirst is a poor indicator of fluid needs. Drink regularly in small amounts. If you postpone drinking, you will have to drink too much too quickly to catch up. By this stage, dehydration may have already set in. Fluid empties more slowly from the stomach when you are dehydrated, so it may even be impossible to catch up while you are still exercising. Drinking small amounts of fluid regularly is far more comfortable than sculling large amounts all at once. The top-up method improves the rate at which fluid leaves the stomach, therefore the rate at which it can be absorbed. The best approach is to start exercise with a comfortably full level of fluid in your stomach and top up this level regularly.

Don't Let Dehydration Cramp Your Style

The cause of cramps is still unknown, however dehydration increases your chance of getting a cramp. Adequate fluid replacement will help to prevent most cramps.

'What about water?'

Water is a great fluid replacer, it is also easy and cheap to obtain. If you exercise for 2 hours or less at a time, drinking plain water to replace fluids is fine. For more prolonged training sessions or competitions, fluid-replacement drinks have the advantage of assisting with refuelling as well as hydration.

Fluid-Replacement Drinks

Experts in the 1970s said water was best, but now the benefits of fluid-replacement drinks for sport are being recognised. These benefits include:

Hydration: The glucose and sodium (salt) in fluid-replacement drinks, enhances water absorption from the intestine. This aids hydration.

Taste: People tend to prefer the flavour of sports drinks over plain water. The pleasant taste encourages them to drink more and replace fluid losses better.

Refuelling: The carbohydrate in fluid-replacement drinks helps to delay fatigue in endurance events. Athletes should aim to drink about 50 g of carbohydrate per hour. They can achieve this by drinking 500-1000 mL/16 fl oz-1¾ pt of a fluid-replacement drink which contains between 5-10% carbohydrate. Refuelling is easier and more rapid from liquids than solids (see page 21 for a list of suitable solid options).

Salt: The sodium in fluid-replacement drinks helps to maintain blood sodium levels in ultra-endurance athletes, where exercise duration and heavy sweating may span over many hours or days. Sodium replacement via a fluid-replacement drink is strongly recommended if the event involves 4 hours or more of strenuous activity.

A fluid-replacement drink only really needs to be a dilute solution of carbohydrate and salt, it does not need to contain fat or protein. Fluid-replacement drinks should ideally contain between 5-10% carbohydrate (5-10 g of carbohydrate per 100 mL/3½ fl oz drink). In newer sports drinks the carbohydrate is usually present as glucose polymers (chains of glucose units).

As too much salt tastes unpleasant, the salt (electrolyte) content of these drinks is generally okay. There are many sports drinks on the market, but not all of these are designed for fluid replacement. When choosing a fluid-replacement drink, read the label carefully and use the above guidelines to help you make the best choice. Drink your fluid-replacement drink cool, not icy cold.

Drinks like soft drink or fruit juice have a higher carbohydrate concentration (12-13%) and therefore empty more slowly from the stomach – they are not the best fluid replacers. These drinks can be used if they are diluted to half strength. Soft drinks should be defizzed (left to go flat) and not contain caffeine.

Rule of thumb

Most well-trained athletes lose around 1 litre/1¾ pt of sweat for each hour of intense physical exercise. You should aim to replace at least two-thirds of this amount whilst exercising. This means drinking about 600-750 mL/ 16 fl oz-1¼ pt of fluid for each hour of strenuous exercise. Remember, if it's hot and/or you sweat heavily, you may need to drink more than this.

GETTING TOO HOT IS NOT COOL

The symptoms of heat stress sneak up on you. Ignoring these symptoms is extremely dangerous, because if you have symptoms you are already quite dehydrated. Don't push yourself to boiling point. These symptoms are your body's way of telling you to stop.

Early warning signs include:
◗ feeling hot and tired
◗ muscle cramps
◗ nausea
◗ difficulties with concentration
◗ headache

As the condition worsens you may:
◗ feel dizzy
◗ become incoherent or disoriented
◗ stop sweating (skin becomes hot and dry)

Making it to the finish line does not prove that you were properly hydrated. Cramps, headaches or nausea after exercise are most likely caused by dehydration. Take heed of these warning signs and make sure that you replace your fluids adequately both during and after the event.

Severe heat stress requires urgent medical attention.

BE STRONG
SAY 'NO' TO ALCOHOL

Alcohol decreases performance. Some athletic people regularly binge on alcohol and still believe that excessive alcohol does not really affect them. Reasons given for excessive drinking include:

'It relaxes me and reduces nervousness'

Alcohol makes you less aware of what is happening, so you may feel more relaxed and less nervous; however, it has this effect on your whole nervous system, so:

your reflexes are slowed
your concentration is dulled
your judgement is impaired

The 'false confidence' you have after drinking alcohol may trick you into thinking you're doing your best when in fact your performance is impaired.

'I train it off or sweat it out'

While you may burn up the kilojoules (calories) alcohol contains, you can't sweat the alcohol out. Excess alcohol can affect many body systems, including:

the brain and nervous system
the heart
the liver

Training cannot reverse these effects. The aim of sports participation is to reach your personal peak, not stay where you are now. To train smart – you must train sober.

'I only drink after the game'

Binge drinking after competition is still common, especially in team sports. Most drinkers think this does no harm as they may 'hardly ever drink at other times'. Binge drinking is as much of a health risk as drinking too much on a regular basis. Exercise beforehand does not reduce your risk. From a fitness and performance point of view, alcohol after strenuous exercise delays recovery. This is because alcohol has a diuretic (dehydrating) effect and also delays the rate of glycogen replenishment. For many, the hangover after an alcohol binge affects their performance at training for several days. The loss of valuable training time is more than they or their team can afford.

Alcohol and injury don't mix

Alcohol dilates blood vessels so it can intensify the swelling and bleeding associated with many sports injuries. A stiff drink may temporarily help you psychologically, but alcohol potentially increases the extent of damage and will delay recovery time. Alcohol should be avoided in all cases of injury for at least 24 hours or until otherwise advised by your doctor.

ALCOHOL

Facts about alcohol you should know include:

▶ You can't sweat it out.
▶ It dehydrates you.
▶ It delays recovery.
▶ It impairs heat regulation.
▶ It slows down glycogen replacement.
▶ It delays recovery from soft tissue (bruising type) injuries.
▶ It depletes the body of important vitamins and minerals.
▶ It slows reaction time and reduces coordination.
▶ It is fattening.
▶ Alcohol is an addictive drug.

Drink Smart

If you drink sensibly, there is no reason why you can't enjoy alcohol regularly. Try these smart drinking tips:

During the week

▶ Enjoy a drink during the week if you compete each weekend.
▶ Drink no more than two standard drinks on any day (see chart).
▶ Try not to drink two days in a row.
▶ If you are watching your weight/body fat levels, try to keep alcohol just for special occasions.

Precompetition

▶ Avoid alcohol 24 hours prior to competition.

After competition

▶ Rehydrate fully (see page 34) before drinking alcohol.
▶ Avoid drinking alcohol in the dressing room.
▶ Start glycogen replacement by consuming carbohydrate-rich foods or drinks as soon as possible after exercise (see page 21 for ideas).
▶ Avoid alcohol if you have been injured.
▶ Drink alcohol with a meal, not on an empty stomach.
▶ Drink a safe level of alcohol. If you have gone over the legal drink-driving limit, you've had too much.

Social ways to drink less

▶ Avoid getting into a 'Round' – why pay for everyone else to get drunk?
▶ Dilute drinks with water, soda or soft drink.
▶ Choose low-alcohol beers.
▶ Offer to drive – it gives you a good reason to drink less.
▶ Set yourself a limit before you start drinking.
▶ Be strong enough to say 'no'.

STANDARD DRINK
Approximately 10 g alcohol

DRINK	10 g ALCOHOL
Regular beer 5% alcohol	200 mL
Light beer 2-3% alcohol	2 × 200 mL
Extra light beer 1% alcohol	5 × 200 mL
Wine /Champagne 10-12% alcohol	100 mL
Spirits 30-40% alcohol	30 mL
Port/Sherry 15-20% alcohol	60 mL
Cider/Stout 5% alcohol	200 mL

CALCIUM
AND OSTEOPOROSIS

Osteoporosis is a condition in which the bones lose calcium, become brittle and tend to break more easily. Our bones reach peak bone strength at about 35 years of age. After this time, bone is gradually lost at a rate of about 1% per year.

▶ Bone loss accelerates in women for 5-10 years after menopause. An increased rate of bone loss may also occur in young athletic women if their menstrual cycle is infrequent or if it stops altogether (a condition known as amenorrhoea). The fall in oestrogen levels associated with cycle cessation is responsible for the increased rate of loss.

▶ Regular strenuous exercise, usually accompanied by other factors such as fat loss, strict dieting or stress, can precipitate cycle interruptions in young female athletes. In these women, the well-known benefits of exercise (particularly weight-bearing exercise such as walking, running and aerobic dance) on bone mass do not outweigh the losses which occur as a result of menstrual irregularity. The benefits of adequate or extra calcium are limited unless the menstrual cycle returns or a program of hormone replacement (usually the oral contraceptive pill in younger women) is undertaken.

▶ Lost bone is not so easy to replace. Menstrual irregularities of greater than six months need medical investigation, ideally by a doctor experienced in dealing with young female athletes. An adequate calcium intake throughout life together with a regular menstrual cycle and weight-bearing exercise is essential to build and then maintain optimal bone strength. Extra calcium in the range of 1000-1500 mg per day is recommended during, and for sometime after, the period of amenorrhoea. Calcium supplements may be needed to help some women reach this daily target.

Other factors detrimental to bone health include:

▶ Cigarette smoking

An excess intake of:

▶ salt;

▶ protein;

▶ caffeine e.g. coffee, tea, cola drinks, chocolate; and

▶ alcohol – two or more standard drinks a day. (See page 36 for standard drinks.)

Three serves of dairy food each day as part of a balanced diet will supply most people with the calcium they need. Calcium can be found in a large number of foods but often only in small amounts. Dairy foods are a richer source of calcium which is generally better absorbed by the body than the calcium from many other foods. There is a wide range of reduced-fat dairy foods to choose from. Low-fat milk and yogurt contain as much calcium as full-fat varieties and fortified milks have even more.

CALCIUM

Age (years)	Daily requirements mg/day	
	Males	Females
8-11	800	900
12-15	1200	900
16-18	1000	1000
19-54	800	800
54-64	800	1000
Pregnant	–	1100
Lactating	–	1200

DAIRY FOOD EQUIVALENTS
To provide 800 mg of calcium

milk 200 mL/6½ fl oz
full-fat 240 mg

yogurt 200 g/6½ oz
full-fat 390 mg

cheese 30 g/1 oz
Cheddar 234 mg

1-2% fat 285 mg
skim 260 mg
fortified 320 mg

non-fat 340 mg

cottage* 300 g = 237 mg
ricotta* 100 g = 245 mg
*reduced-fat varieties

Use the table above to work out your calcium requirements. If necessary, add in extra servings of dairy food to reach your daily target.
Note: 200 mL/6½ fl oz fortified soy milk has 290 mg calcium. This is the best substitute if you are unable to eat dairy food.

DINNER
DELICIOUS WAYS TO RECHARGE

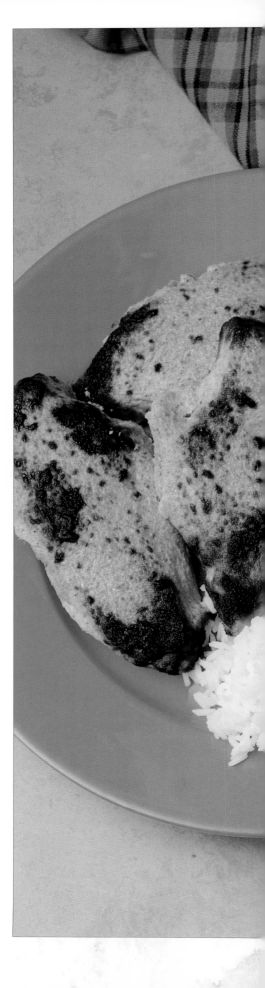

Tandoori Chicken

Serves 6

Oven temp: 180°C, 350°F, Gas 4

6 boneless chicken breast fillets, skin removed

TANDOORI PASTE
2 teaspoons ground cumin
I teaspoon ground coriander
¹/₂ teaspoon ground cardamom
I teaspoon grated fresh ginger
¹/₂ teaspoon ground turmeric
¹/₂ teaspoon chilli powder
I cup/200 g/6¹/₂ oz low-fat yogurt

1   To make Tandoori Paste, place cumin, coriander, cardamom, ginger, turmeric and chilli powder in a bowl and mix to combine. Add yogurt and mix to make a paste.

2   Place chicken in a shallow glass or ceramic dish, spoon over Tandoori Paste and turn to coat. Cover and set aside to marinate for 2 hours.

3   Remove chicken from Tandoori Paste, place in a baking dish and bake for 20-30 minutes or until chicken is cooked.

Serving suggestion: For a complete meal, serve Tandoori Chicken with rice and salad.

585 kilojoules (140 Calories) per serve
Carbohydrate	2 g (6%)	low
Fat	4 g	very low

Tandoori Lamb
Replace chicken fillets with 6 lamb fillets or lamb leg steaks.

975 kilojoules (235 Calories) per serve
Carbohydrate	2 g (3%)	low
Fat	7 g	low

Nachos

Serves 4
Oven temp: 180°C, 350°F, Gas 4

I quantity Spicy Beans (see page 46)
2 teaspoons chilli sauce
I quantity plain Pitta Crisps (see page 14)
60 g/2 oz grated reduced-fat mozzarella cheese
4 tablespoons low-fat natural yogurt

1   Make up Spicy Beans following recipe, adding chilli sauce.

2   Make up Pitta Crisps following recipe.

3   Place Pitta Crisps in an ovenproof baking dish, spoon over Spicy Beans and sprinkle with cheese. Bake for 10-15 minutes or microwave on HIGH (100%) for 2-3 minutes or until cheese melts. Serve with yogurt.

2355 kilojoules (560 Calories) per serve
Carbohydrate	77 g (54%)	medium
Fat	13 g	medium

Beef Skewers

Serves 4

750 g/1¹/₂ lb rump steak, cut into thin strips
2 cups/440 g/14 oz rice, cooked

HONEY MARINADE
I clove garlic, crushed
2 tablespoons honey
2 teaspoons curry powder
I tablespoon soy sauce

1   To make marinade, place garlic, honey, curry powder and soy sauce in a bowl and mix to combine. Add beef and toss to coat. Cover and set aside to marinate for 1 hour.

2   Preheat grill or barbecue to a medium-high heat. Thread beef strips on skewers and cook under grill or on barbecue, turning occasionally, for 4-5 minutes or until cooked to your liking. Serve with rice.

2605 kilojoules (620 Calories) per serve
Carbohydrate	91 g (58%)	high
Fat	5 g	low

Nachos, Beef Skewers, Tandoori Chicken

White Plate Pillivuyt   Blue and Orange Plates Limoges

Pasta with Tomato, Chilli and Herb Sauce

Serves 4

500 g/1 lb pasta of your choice
TOMATO, CHILLI AND
HERB SAUCE
1 onion, chopped
2 cloves garlic, crushed
2 x 440 g/14 oz canned tomatoes,
undrained and mashed
3 tablespoons tomato paste (purée)
2 teaspoons chilli sauce
1 red pepper, chopped
1 green pepper, chopped
1 tablespoon chopped fresh basil
1 tablespoon chopped fresh parsley
freshly ground black pepper

1 Cook pasta in boiling water in a
large saucepan following packet
instructions. Drain, set aside and
keep warm.

2 To make sauce, place onion and
garlic in a nonstick frying pan and
cook, stirring, over a medium heat
for 2-3 minutes or until soft.

3 Stir in tomatoes, tomato paste
(purée), chilli sauce, red pepper,
green pepper, basil, parsley and
black pepper to taste and simmer
for 10 minutes or until sauce
reduces and thickens slightly.
Spoon sauce over pasta and serve
immediately.

1760 kilojoules (420 Calories) per serve
Carbohydrate   84.5 g (81%)   very high
Fat   1.5 g   very low

Pasta with Marinara Sauce

Serves 4

500 g/1 lb pasta of your choice
MARINARA SAUCE
8 large uncooked prawns, shelled and
deveined, tails left intact
8 mussels
1 tablespoon lemon juice
1 calamari (squid) tube, sliced
4 baby octopus, cleaned and chopped
1 quantity Tomato Chilli and Herb Sauce
(see recipe above) or 750 mL/1¼ pt jar
prepared tomato pasta sauce

1 Cook pasta in boiling water in a
large saucepan following packet
instructions. Drain, set aside and
keep warm.

2 To make sauce, place prawns,
mussels and lemon juice in a
nonstick frying pan and cook,
stirring, over a medium-high heat for
3-4 minutes or until prawns just
change colour and are almost
cooked. Add calamari (squid) and
cook, stirring, for 1 minute longer.

3 Stir in sauce, bring to simmering
and cook for 2-3 minutes or until
heated through. Spoon sauce over
pasta and serve immediately.

2480 kilojoules (590 Calories) per serve
Carbohydrate   86 g (58%)   high
Fat   7 g   low

Pasta with Cheese Sauce

Serves 4

500 g/1 lb pasta of your choice
45 g/1½ oz grated Parmesan cheese
45 g/1½ oz grated reduced-fat Cheddar
cheese

BASIC WHITE SAUCE
1½ cups/375 mL/12 fl oz reduced-fat milk
½ cup/125 mL/4 fl oz chicken stock
½ teaspoon dry mustard
1½ tablespoons cornflour blended with
2 tablespoons water
freshly ground black pepper

1 Cook pasta in boiling water in a
large saucepan following packet
instructions. Drain, set aside and
keep warm.

2 To make sauce, place milk,
stock and mustard in a saucepan
and cook, stirring occasionally, over
a medium heat for 4-5 minutes or
until almost boiling. Stir in cornflour
mixture and cook, stirring
constantly, until sauce boils and
thickens. Season to taste with black
pepper.

3 Add Parmesan and Cheddar
cheeses to sauce and stir until
cheeses melt. Spoon sauce over
pasta and serve immediately.

2030 kilojoules (485 Calories) per serve
Carbohydrate   82.5 g (68%)   high
Fat   7 g   low

Pasta with Mushroom and Ham Sauce

Serves 4

500 g/1 lb pasta of your choice
MUSHROOM AND HAM SAUCE
300 g/9½ oz button mushrooms, sliced
4 spring onions, chopped
4 slices reduced-fat-and-salt ham, chopped
½ cup/125 mL/4 fl oz dry white wine
1 quantity Basic White Sauce (see recipe
this page), heated
freshly ground black pepper

1 Cook pasta in boiling water in a
large saucepan following packet
instructions. Drain, set aside and
keep warm.

2 Place mushrooms, spring onions
and ham in a nonstick frying pan
and cook, stirring, over high heat for
4-5 minutes or until mushrooms are
cooked.

3 Stir in wine, bring to simmering
and simmer for 2 minutes.

4 Stir mushroom mixture into white
sauce and cook, stirring, for 1-2
minutes. Season to taste with black
pepper. Spoon sauce over pasta
and serve immediately.

2050 kilojoules (490 Calories) per serve
Carbohydrate   84 g (69%)   high
Fat   4 g   very low

REDUCING SALT

▶ Avoid the addition of salt to
food – use herbs and spices for
flavour.
▶ Reduce consumption of salty
foods such as processed meats
and snack foods.
▶ Include some salt-reduced
products in your diet.

Pasta with Mushroom and Ham Sauce, Pasta
with Tomato, Chilli and Herb Sauce, Pasta
with Marinara Sauce, Pasta with Cheese Sauce

Lean Roast

Serves 6

Oven temp: 190°C, 375°F, Gas 5

750 g/1½ lb beef fillet
2 cloves garlic, crushed
2 teaspoons crushed black peppercorns
water

ROAST VEGETABLES
18 large potatoes, halved
6 slices pumpkin
6 pieces sweet potato

GRAVY
2 tablespoons instant gravy powder
½ cup/125 mL/4 fl oz water
½ cup/125 mL/4 fl oz red wine
1 tablespoon Worcestershire sauce

1   To cook vegetables, place potatoes, pumpkin and sweet potato on a nonstick oven tray or a tray lined with nonstick baking paper and bake, turning once, for 1 hour or until vegetables are tender and golden.

2   Rub beef with garlic and black peppercorns and place on a wire rack set in a baking dish. Pour enough water into baking dish to come within 1 cm/½ in of the rack and bake for 40-45 minutes or until beef is cooked to your liking.

3   To make gravy, place instant gravy powder, water, wine and Worcestershire sauce in a small saucepan and cook over a medium heat, stirring constantly, until gravy thickens.

4   To serve, cut meat into slices and accompany with steamed green vegetables and gravy.

Nutrition tip: Add extra potatoes or bread to this meal to boost the carbohydrate. You might like to try Quick Fruit Bread Pudding (page 66) for dessert.

1730 kilojoules (415 Calories) per serve

Carbohydrate	*49 g (47%)*	*low*
Fat	*6 g*	*low*

Lean Roast

ABSORBING FACTS ABOUT IRON

The amount of iron in food as well as the amount that can be absorbed, from food varies. 'Flesh' foods such as offal (liver and kidneys), red meat, poultry and seafood, contain **haem iron**. This iron is well absorbed by the body. Kidneys, liver and red meat are the richest sources of haem iron.

Plant foods such as bread, breakfast cereal, rice, pasta, fruits and vegetables generally contain less iron than flesh foods. The iron in plant foods is less well absorbed because it is in a **non-haem** form. Dried peas and beans (kidney, baked, soy and the like) are the richest 'vegetarian' sources of iron.

'How do I know if I'm iron deficient?'

Fatigue and lethargy are the early symptoms of iron deficiency anaemia. Dizziness, shortness of breath and palpitations may be experienced if deficiency is severe.

A medical diagnosis of anaemia is made from a blood test which measures haemoglobin, iron stores (ferritin) and a number of other blood components. Iron stores fall first, so they are often used to detect the very early stages of deficiency. Athletic performance may be impaired, even in the early stages of iron deficiency.

'Do I need an iron supplement?'

Iron supplements are required if a blood test confirms iron deficiency. Once iron levels are restored, an improved iron intake will help to prevent deficiency in the future. Iron supplements are a form of medication and should be taken under the supervision of your doctor or dietitian – not on self prescription. Regular blood tests are necessary to determine if there is an adequate response to treatment and then later to detect any subsequent deficiency promptly.

Iron Boosters

Eat:
▶ Meat, chicken or fish daily
▶ Red meat 3 or more times a week
▶ Liver and kidneys regularly

For vegetarians:
▶ Dried peas and beans daily
▶ Vitamin C containing foods with meals
▶ Vitamin C improves absorption of non-haem iron sources
▶ Vitamin C rich foods include oranges, melons, kiwifruit, red and green peppers

Iron Reducers

Try to avoid the iron-reducers which reduce iron absorption from non-flesh (non-haem) iron sources.

▶ Caffeine in coffee, tea, chocolate, chocolate drinks and cola drinks
▶ Tannin in tea
▶ Phytate found in unprocessed bran

Helpful hints
Try herbal teas or decaffeinated coffee. Reduce the number of cups of caffeine-containing drinks consumed.

Thai Beef

Serves 4

500 g/1 lb rump steak, sliced
1 stalk fresh lemon grass, chopped
or 2 teaspoons finely grated lemon rind
1 teaspoon grated fresh ginger
1 fresh red chilli, finely chopped
1 tablespoon chopped fresh coriander
1 tablespoon lime rind
1 tablespoon lime juice
2 tablespoons desiccated coconut
1/2 cup/125 mL/4 fl oz beef stock
2 teaspoons cornflour blended
with 1 tablespoon water
2 cups/440 g/14 oz rice, cooked

1   Heat a nonstick frying pan over
high heat, add beef and stir-fry for
4-5 minutes or until meat is brown.

2   Add lemon grass or lemon rind,
ginger, chilli, coriander, lime rind,
lime juice, coconut, stock and
cornflour mixture and cook, stirring,
over a high heat until mixture boils
and thickens. Spoon beef mixture
over hot rice and serve.

2580 kilojoules (615 Calories) per serve

Carbohydrate	90.5 g (52%)	medium
Fat	10 g	medium

Fruity Pork

Serves 4

500 g/1 lb lean pork, cut into cubes
1 apple, peeled and grated
250 g/8 oz broccoli florets
1 red pepper, chopped
155 g/5 oz green beans, trimmed and
halved
45 g/1 1/2 oz chopped dried apricots
1 cup/250 mL/8 fl oz apricot nectar or
orange juice
1/2 cup/125 mL/4 fl oz chicken stock
1 tablespoon cornflour blended
with 2 tablespoons water
500 g/1 lb noodles, cooked

1   Heat a nonstick frying pan or
wok over a high heat, add pork and
stir-fry for 4-5 minutes or until brown
and tender.

2   Add apple, broccoli, red pepper,
beans and dried apricots to pan and
stir-fry for 2-3 minutes or until
vegetables are tender crisp.

3   Combine apricot nectar or
orange juice, stock and cornflour
mixture, add to pan and cook,
stirring, for 1 minute or until sauce
boils and thickens. Spoon pork
mixture over hot noodles and serve
immediately.

2815 kilojoules (670 Calories) per serve

Carbohydrate	96 g (57%)	high
Fat	8 g	low

Chilli Chicken Stir-Fry

Serves 4

6 spring onions, finely chopped
4 boneless chicken breast fillets, cut
into strips
1 clove garlic, crushed
3 tablespoons sweet chilli sauce
3 tablespoons tomato purée
250 g/8 oz snow peas (mangetout),
trimmed
1 red pepper, sliced
2 zucchini (courgettes), sliced
500 g/1 lb pasta, cooked

1   Heat nonstick frying pan or wok
over a high heat, add spring onions,
chicken and garlic and stir-fry for 3-4
minutes or until chicken is tender.

2   Stir in chilli sauce, tomato purée,
snow peas (mangetout), red pepper
and zucchini (courgettes) and stir-fry
for 2-3 minutes longer or until
vegetables are tender crisp. To
serve, spoon vegetable mixture
over hot pasta.

2185 kilojoules (520 Calories) per serve

Carbohydrate	80 g (61%)	high
Fat	5 g	low

Vegetable Stir-Fry

Serves 4

2 cloves garlic, crushed
2 onions, sliced
1 parsnip, sliced
2 carrots, chopped
2 stalks celery, chopped
1 eggplant (aubergine), finely chopped
8 stalks spinach, shredded
1 red pepper, chopped
250 g/8 oz broccoli florets
3 tablespoons honey
2 tablespoons poppy seeds
500 g/1 lb pasta, cooked

1   Heat a nonstick frying pan or
wok over a medium-high heat, add
garlic and onions and stir-fry for 2-3
minutes or until onions are soft.

2   Add parsnip, carrots, celery,
eggplant (aubergine), spinach, red
pepper and broccoli and stir-fry for
3-4 minutes or until vegetables are
tender crisp.

3   Stir in honey and poppy seeds
and cook for 1 minute longer.
Spoon vegetable mixture over hot
pasta and serve immediately.

Nutrition tip: To boost carbohydrate,
increase the serving size of rice,
pasta or noodles.

1990 kilojoules (475 Calories) per serve

Carbohydrate	99 g (83%)	very high
Fat	1.5 g	very low

Blue and White Plate and Cloth Country Road   Small Plate Inner City Clayworkers Gallery   Green Plate Basic Essentials

Curry Lamb Stir-Fry

Serves 4

500 g/1 lb lamb eye loin or lean lamb, trimmed
1 tablespoon mild curry paste
2 onions, sliced into wedges
250 g/8 oz cauliflower florets
1 green pepper, chopped
2 carrots, sliced
1 cup/250 mL/8 fl oz beef stock
1 tablespoon cornflour blended with 1½ tablespoons water
60 g/2 oz sultanas
2 cups/440 g/14 oz rice, cooked

1   Cut lamb into 5 mm/¼ in slices. Heat a nonstick frying pan or wok over a high heat, add lamb and stir-fry for 2-3 minutes or until tender.

2   Remove lamb from pan and set aside. Add curry paste and onions to pan and stir-fry for 2-3 minutes or until onions are soft.

3   Add cauliflower, green pepper and carrots to pan and stir-fry for 2 minutes.

4   Stir beef stock and cornflour mixture into pan and cook, stirring, for 2 minutes or until sauce boils and thickens slightly. Return lamb to pan, add sultanas and cook for 1 minute or until heated through. Spoon lamb mixture over hot rice and serve immediately.

Cook's tip: When stir-frying meat that has been cut into strips or small pieces it is essential to preheat the pan or wok over a high heat before adding the meat. Doing this seals in the juices and the meat will be more tender.

2830 kilojoules (675 Calories) per serve

Carbohydrate	*98 g (57%)*	*high*
Fat	*10 g*	*medium*

Fruity Pork, Curry Lamb Stir-Fry, Thai Beef, Chilli Chicken Stir-Fry, Vegetable Stir-Fry

Vegetable Lasagne

Serves 4
Oven temp: 180°C, 350°F, Gas 4

250 g/8 oz broccoli florets
250 g/8 oz cauliflower florets
125 g/4 oz green beans, sliced
1 red pepper, chopped
2 zucchini (courgettes), sliced
2 carrots, sliced
440 g/14 oz canned tomato purée
2 tablespoons chopped fresh parsley
2 teaspoons chilli sauce
12 sheets instant spinach lasagne
45 g/1½ oz grated Parmesan cheese
45 g/1½ oz grated reduced-fat Cheddar cheese

WHITE SAUCE
2 cups/500 mL/16 fl oz reduced-fat milk
2 tablespoons cornflour blended
with 3 tablespoons water
1 teaspoon prepared mild mustard
freshly ground black pepper

1   Heat a large nonstick frying pan over a medium-high heat, add broccoli, cauliflower, beans, red pepper, zucchini (courgettes), carrots, tomato purée, parsley and chilli sauce, bring to simmering and simmer for 6-8 minutes or until vegetables are tender. Remove pan from heat and set aside.

2   To make sauce, place milk in a saucepan and heat over a medium heat, stirring occasionally, for 4-5 minutes or until almost boiling. Stir in cornflour mixture and cook, stirring constantly, for 3-4 minutes or until sauce boils and thickens. Stir in mustard and season to taste with black pepper.

3   Line an ovenproof dish with 4 lasagne sheets, top with one-third of the vegetable mixture, and one-third of the sauce. Repeat layers, finishing with a layer of sauce. Combine Parmesan and Cheddar cheeses, sprinkle over top of lasagne and bake for 30 minutes or until lasagne sheets are soft.

1670 kilojoules (400 Calories) per serve

Carbohydrate	*57 g (56%)*	*high*
Fat	*9 g*	*low*

Lite Lasagne

Serves 4
Oven temp: 180°C, 350°F, Gas 4

1 onion, chopped
350 g/11 oz lean beef mince
440 g/14 oz canned tomatoes, undrained and mashed
3 tablespoons tomato paste (purée)
½ cup/125 mL/4 fl oz beef stock
freshly ground black pepper
12 sheets instant lasagne
500 g/1 lb low-fat cottage cheese
45 g/1½ oz grated reduced-fat Cheddar cheese

1   Heat a nonstick frying pan over a high heat, add onion and cook for 2-3 minutes or until soft. Stir in beef and cook, stirring frequently, for 4-5 minutes or until well browned.

2   Add tomatoes, tomato paste (purée) and beef stock to pan, bring to simmering and cook, stirring frequently, for 4-5 minutes. Season to taste with black pepper.

3   Line an ovenproof dish with 4 lasagne sheets, top with one-third of the meat mixture and one third of the cottage cheese. Repeat layers finishing with a layer of cottage cheese.

4   Sprinkle top of lasagne with Cheddar cheese and bake for 35-40 minutes or until lasagne sheets are soft.

Serving suggestion: For a complete meal serve lasagne with salad or vegetables and crusty bread.

Nutrition tip: To remove as much fat as possible from mince, after browning remove it from the pan, place on absorbent kitchen paper and allow to drain. Alternatively push the mince to one side of the pan and drain off any fat that has come out during browning. Remember when buying mince to choose the leanest available or buy a lean cut of meat and mince your own.

1645 kilojoules (390 Calories) per serve

Carbohydrate	*41 g (28%)*	*low*
Fat	*13 g*	*medium*

Spicy Bean Lasagne

Serves 4
Oven temp: 180°C, 350°F, Gas 4

12 sheets instant lasagne
375 g/12 oz low-fat ricotta or cottage cheese
45 g/1½ oz grated reduced-fat mozzarella cheese

SPICY BEANS
1 onion, chopped
1 teaspoon ground cumin
1 teaspoon ground coriander
440 g/14 oz canned red kidney beans, rinsed and drained
440 g/14 oz canned tomatoes, undrained and mashed
2 tablespoons tomato paste (purée)

1   For Spicy Beans, heat a nonstick frying pan over a medium-high heat, add onion and cook, stirring, for 2 minutes or until soft. Stir in cumin and coriander and cook for 1 minute longer.

2   Add beans, tomatoes and tomato paste (purée) to pan, bring to simmering and simmer for 4 minutes or until bean mixture thickens slightly.

3   Line the base of an ovenproof dish with 4 lasagne sheets, top with one-third of the bean mixture and one-third of the ricotta or cottage cheese. Repeat layers finishing with a layer of ricotta or cottage cheese. Sprinkle with mozzarella cheese and bake for 30-35 minutes or until lasagne sheets are soft.

1750 kilojoules (420 Calories) per serve

Carbohydrate	*53 g (25%)*	*low*
Fat	*12 g*	*medium*

Vegetable Lasagne, Spicy Bean Lasagne, Lite Lasagne

Chicken and Parmesan Risotto

Serves 4

4 cups/1 litre/1¾ pt chicken stock
2 cups/500 mL/16 fl oz water
2 cups/440 g/14 oz short-grain rice
90 g/3 oz chopped cooked chicken
2 tablespoons snipped fresh chives
60 g/2 oz grated Parmesan cheese
freshly ground black pepper

1   Place stock and water in a large saucepan and heat over a medium heat until boiling. Place rice in a nonstick frying pan and cook, stirring, over a low heat for 3 minutes.

2   Gradually pour 1 cup/250 mL/8 fl oz stock mixture into rice and cook, stirring, until liquid is absorbed. Repeat this process until all stock mixture is used.

3   Add chicken, chives, Parmesan cheese and black pepper to taste to rice mixture and mix well to combine. Serve immediately.

2035 kilojoules (485 Calories) per serve
Carbohydrate	80 g (65%)	high
Fat	7 g	low

Spiced Rice

Serves 4

2 cups/440 g/14 oz rice
8 cups/2 litres/3½ pt boiling water
1 cinnamon stick
4 cardamom pods
6 coriander seeds
2 whole cloves
1 tablespoon orange juice
rind 1 orange, cut into strips
rind 1 lemon, cut into strips
60 g/2 oz currants
1 tablespoon chopped fresh coriander

1   Place rice, boiling water, cinnamon stick, cardamom pods, coriander seeds and cloves into a large saucepan, bring to the boil and boil for 10-12 minutes or until rice is tender. Drain rice and remove spices.

2   Place orange juice and orange rind and lemon rind in a saucepan and cook over a low heat for 2 minutes or until soft. Stir in currants, fresh coriander and rice and cook over a medium heat, stirring, for 2 minutes or until heated through. Serve immediately.

2030 kilojoules (485 Calories) per serve
Carbohydrate	109 g (91%)	very high
Fat	0.5 g	very low

Speedy Paella

Serves 4

2 boneless chicken breast fillets, skinned and cut into strips
8 large uncooked prawns, shelled and deveined
4 slices reduced-fat-and-salt ham, sliced
2 cups/440 g/14 oz rice, cooked
pinch ground turmeric
½ cup/125 mL/4 fl oz chicken stock
60 g/2 oz fresh or frozen peas
2 tablespoons chopped fresh parsley
freshly ground black pepper

1   Heat a nonstick frying pan over a high heat, add chicken and stir-fry for 4-5 minutes or until tender. Remove chicken from pan and set aside.

2   Add prawns to pan and stir-fry for 2-3 minutes or until prawns change colour and are cooked through.

3   Return chicken to pan, add ham, rice, turmeric, stock, peas and parsley and cook, stirring, for 3 minutes or until heated through. Serve immediately. Season to taste with black pepper.

2005 kilojoules (475 Calories) per serve
Carbohydrate	81 g (68%)	high
Fat	4 g	very low

Rice Pie

Serves 4
Oven temp: 180°C, 350°F, Gas 4

2 cups/440 g/14 oz rice, cooked
½ cup/60 g/2 oz flour
4 egg whites
3 tablespoons tomato paste (purée)
2 tablespoons vegetable stock or water
12 button mushrooms, sliced
1 red pepper, finely chopped
4 spring onions, chopped
1 carrot, grated
2 tablespoons chopped fresh parsley
2 tablespoons sweet chilli sauce (optional)
freshly ground black pepper

1   Place rice, flour, egg whites and tomato paste (purée) in a bowl and mix well to combine.

2   Place stock in a large frying pan and heat over a low heat, add mushrooms, red pepper, spring onions, carrot, parsley, chilli sauce (if using) and black pepper to taste and cook, stirring frequently, for 4-5 minutes or until vegetables are soft.

3   Remove vegetables from pan and set aside to cool slightly. Add vegetable mixture to rice and mix to combine. Spoon rice mixture into a 23 cm/9 in springform tin, lined wtih nonstick baking paper and bake for 30-40 minutes or until firm.

1895 kilojoules (452 Calories) per serve
Carbohydrate	96 g (85%)	very high
Fat	2 g	very low

Fried Rice

Serves 4

2 eggs, lightly beaten
6 spring onions, chopped
4 slices reduced-fat-and-salt ham, chopped
1 red pepper, chopped
440 g/14 oz canned sweet corn kernels, drained
2 cups/440 g/14 oz rice, cooked
3 tablespoons low-salt soy sauce
2 teaspoons chilli sauce

1   Place eggs and spring onions in a bowl and mix to combine. Heat a nonstick frying pan over a medium heat, pour egg mixture into pan and cook for 2-3 minutes or until set. Remove omelette from pan, roll up, slice and set aside.

2   Wipe pan clean, heat over a medium heat, add ham, red pepper, sweet corn, rice, soy sauce and chilli sauce and stir-fry for 4-5 minutes or until heated through. Add egg strips and toss to combine. Serve immediately.

Microwave it: Cooking rice in the microwave does not save time but it is foolproof and there are no messy saucepans. It is also the perfect way to cook rice for fried rice. To cook rice in the microwave, place 2 cups/440 g/14 oz rice and 4 cups/1 litre/1¾ pt water in a large microwave-safe dish and cook, uncovered, on HIGH (100%) for 15-20 minutes or until liquid is absorbed and rice is tender. Fluff up with a fork and use as desired.

2235 kilojoules (535 Calories) per serve
Carbohydrate	102 g (76%)	very high
Fat	5 g	low

Fried Rice, Chicken and Parmesan Risotto, Spiced Rice, Rice Pie, Speedy Paella

FAT
THE HIDDEN OPPONENT

Fat is not always as visible as butter, margarine, the fat on meat, the skin on chicken or the oil we cook in or dress our salads with.

Much of the fat that we eat is hidden inside foods such as cakes, biscuits, confectionery, pies, pastries and fast food. We unknowingly eat more fat than we see. To confuse matters further, fat comes in different types. We need to be aware of which types are best for health and the types that are in different foods.

The Good, the Bad and the Ugly

Triglycerides and cholesterol are two distinctly different fatty type substances in our diet. Triglycerides are such a large and diverse group of fats that they can be classified into three main types:

Saturated fat
Mono-unsaturated fat
Polyunsaturated fat

Of all the fats we eat, research points to the mono-unsaturated and polyunsaturated fats as being the 'good' fats, especially in relation to blood cholesterol levels.

Cholesterol itself is found in foods such as eggs, offal, meat, shellfish, chicken and dairy products. More emphasis is often placed on the cholesterol in foods than the fat, hence the pre-occupation with the label 'Cholesterol Free'. Although eating too much cholesterol is still considered a bad practice, it is the saturated fat in food that increases blood cholesterol levels even more than eating cholesterol itself.

Saturated fat is the 'ugly' dietary fat. Use the 'Finding Fat in Foods' graph opposite to see the amount and type of fat in some popular foods.

FAT-REDUCTION QUIZ

		Yes	No
1	I mostly use reduced-fat dairy products.	☐	☐
2	I always cut the fat off meat.	☐	☐
3	I always remove the skin from chicken.	☐	☐
4	I fry food no more than once a week.	☐	☐
5	I eat high-fat snack foods such as potato crisps, chocolate and french fries, no more than once a week.	☐	☐
6	I spread butter or margarine thinly on bread, or use none at all.	☐	☐
7	If I use oil, I use less than 1 tablespoon for 4 serves. (Tick YES if you don't use oil.)	☐	☐
8	I cook in polyunsaturated or mono-unsaturated oil (olive or canola) instead of butter or dripping. (Tick YES if you don't cook in fat/oil.)	☐	☐
9	I avoid salad dressings or use no-oil varieties.	☐	☐
10	I snack on bread, fruit and cereals in preference to biscuits and cake.	☐	☐
11	I avoid cream.	☐	☐
12	I avoid using butter, margarine or sour cream on vegetables.	☐	☐
	TOTAL		_____

Scoring: For each YES answer SCORE 1 point – the higher your score the better.

FINDING FAT IN FOODS

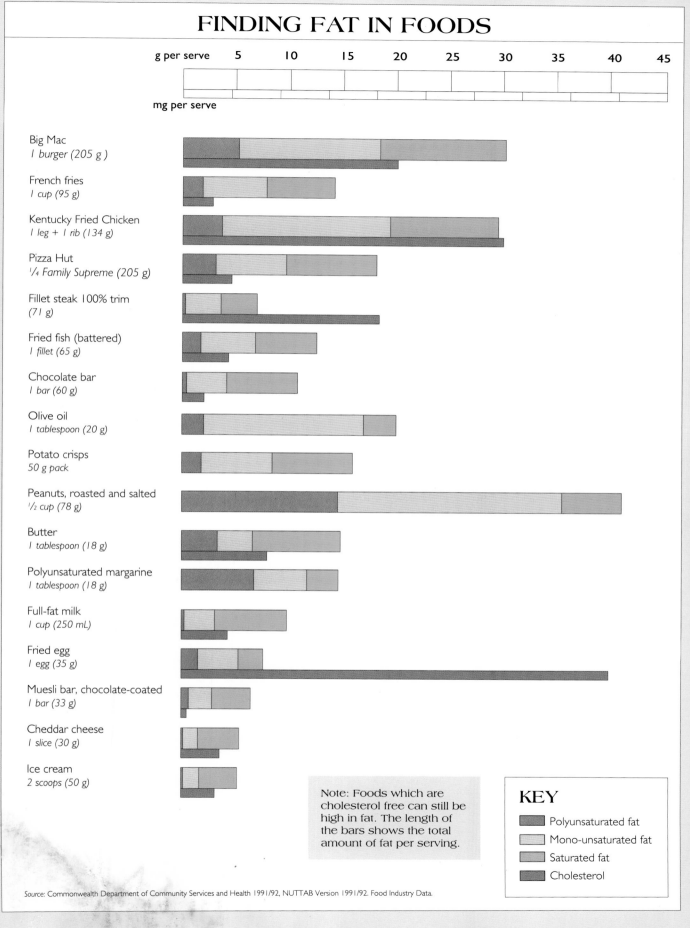

| g per serve | 5 | 10 | 15 | 20 | 25 | 30 | 35 | 40 | 45 |

mg per serve

Big Mac
1 burger (205 g)

French fries
1 cup (95 g)

Kentucky Fried Chicken
1 leg + 1 rib (134 g)

Pizza Hut
¼ Family Supreme (205 g)

Fillet steak 100% trim
(71 g)

Fried fish (battered)
1 fillet (65 g)

Chocolate bar
1 bar (60 g)

Olive oil
1 tablespoon (20 g)

Potato crisps
50 g pack

Peanuts, roasted and salted
½ cup (78 g)

Butter
1 tablespoon (18 g)

Polyunsaturated margarine
1 tablespoon (18 g)

Full-fat milk
1 cup (250 mL)

Fried egg
1 egg (35 g)

Muesli bar, chocolate-coated
1 bar (33 g)

Cheddar cheese
1 slice (30 g)

Ice cream
2 scoops (50 g)

Note: Foods which are cholesterol free can still be high in fat. The length of the bars shows the total amount of fat per serving.

KEY

- Polyunsaturated fat
- Mono-unsaturated fat
- Saturated fat
- Cholesterol

Source: Commonwealth Department of Community Services and Health 1991/92, NUTTAB Version 1991/92. Food Industry Data.

FAST FOOD
MADE AT HOME

Herb and Onion Pizzas

Serves 4
Oven temp: 180°C, 350°F, Gas 4

4 x 15 cm/6 in squares focaccia (ciabatta) bread

HERB AND ONION TOPPING
2 red onions, sliced
1 onion, sliced
2 cloves garlic, crushed
freshly ground black pepper
1 tablespoon vinegar
3 tablespoons low-oil mayonnaise
2 tablespoons chopped fresh parsley
2 tablespoons chopped fresh basil
90 g/3 oz reduced-fat mozzarella

1   To make topping, heat a nonstick frying pan over a high heat, add red onions and onion and cook, stirring, for 4-5 minutes or until golden. Add garlic and cook for 1 minute longer. Season with black pepper to taste.

2   Stir vinegar into onion mixture. Remove pan from heat and stir in mayonnaise, parsley and basil.

3   Top each focaccia (ciabatta) square with one-quarter of the onion mixture. Sprinkle mozzarella cheese over onion mixture and bake for 20 minutes or until cheese is melted and golden.

2570 kilojoules (615 Calories) per serve
Carbohydrate   94 g (58%)   high
Fat   14 g   medium

Sweet and Sour Chicken

Serves 4

4 boneless chicken breast fillets, skinned and cut into strips
6 spring onions, sliced
1 cucumber, chopped
1 green pepper, chopped
155 g/5 oz bean sprouts
440 g/14 oz canned pineapple pieces in natural juice, drained and juice reserved
2 cups/440 g/14 oz rice, cooked

SWEET AND SOUR SAUCE
2 tablespoons tomato sauce
1/4 cup/60 mL/2 fl oz vinegar
1 cup/250 mL/8 fl oz chicken stock
1 1/2 tablespoons cornflour blended with 1 1/2 tablespoons water

1   Heat a nonstick frying pan or wok over a high heat, add chicken strips and stir-fry for 3-4 minutes or until golden and tender.

2   Add spring onions, cucumber, green pepper and bean sprouts and stir-fry for 2 minutes.

3   To make sauce, combine tomato sauce, vinegar, stock, cornflour mixture and reserved pineapple juice. Stir sauce and pineapple pieces into chicken mixture and cook, stirring, for 2-3 minutes or until sauce boils and thickens. Serve with hot rice.

2500 kilojoules (595 Calories) per serve
Carbohydrate   105 g (70%)   very high
Fat   4.5 g   very low

Hamburgers

Serves 4

4 hamburger buns, split and toasted
8 lettuce leaves
8 slices tomato
8 slices beetroot
4 slices reduced-fat Cheddar cheese

MEAT PATTIE
350 g/11 oz lean beef mince
1 cup/60 g/2 oz breadcrumbs, made from stale bread
1 egg, lightly beaten
2 tablespoons Worcestershire sauce
freshly ground black pepper

1   To make patties place beef, breadcrumbs, egg, Worcestershire sauce and black pepper to taste in a bowl and mix well to combine.

2   Divide meat mixture into four portions and shape into patties. Heat a nonstick frying pan over a medium heat and cook patties for 4-5 minutes each side or until cooked to your liking.

3   Top bottom half of each bun with a pattie, 2 lettuce leaves, 2 slices tomato, 2 slices beetroot and 1 slice cheese and top half of bun. Serve immediately.

1915 kilojoules (455 Calories) per serve
Carbohydrate   40 g (35%)   low
Fat   17 g   high

Herb and Onion Pizza, Hamburgers, Sweet and Sour Chicken

Fat and alcohol are your biggest threats when you eat out. The following strategies will help you to head off the 'overdone it' hangover, yet still have a great time.

▶ Ask for plain bread (no butter). Avoid garlic and herb bread, which is usually soaked in butter.

▶ Watch out for dressings and creamy or cheese sauces which are sometimes added – order a brown or tomato-based sauce instead.

▶ Choose barbecued or grilled rather than pan-fried or deep-fried foods.

▶ Trim the fat off meat and take the skin off chicken. Watch out for French fries – instead order plain vegetables or salad (without dressing if possible).

▶ Ask for your food to be cooked in a low-fat way. You will find that most restaurants try their best to help you.

▶ Order a jug of water for your table – you will drink less alcohol and keep yourself better hydrated.

▶ Skip the pre-dinner drinks. Plan to have only 1 or 2 alcoholic drinks with the meal.

▶ Order less food. One or two courses should be ample. Alternatively, you can order two first courses and cut down that way.

▶ Try a vegetable soup or salad for the first course.

▶ Ask what accompaniments come with the main course – you can then avoid being tempted by chips, buttered vegetables and the like. Ask for lower fat alternatives when you order.

▶ Order extra bread instead of chips.

Pitta Pizzas

Serves 4
Oven temp: 180°C, 350°F, Gas 4

4 small pitta bread rounds

PIZZA TOPPING
1/2 cup/125 mL/4 fl oz prepared tomato pasta sauce or tomato paste (purée)
1 small red pepper, sliced
250 g/8 oz canned pineapple pieces, drained
2 slices reduced-fat-and-salt ham, cut into strips
8 button mushrooms, sliced
90 g/3 oz grated reduced-fat Cheddar cheese

1 Place bread rounds on nonstick baking trays and spread each with tomato sauce or paste (purée).

2 Top bread rounds with red pepper, pineapple, ham, mushrooms and cheese and bake for 15-20 minutes or until pizzas are crisp and cheese is melted and golden.

1110 kilojoules (265 Calories) per serve
Carbohydrate	34 g (50%)	medium
Fat	7.5 g	low

Chicken Pizzas

Serves 4
Oven temp: 180°C, 350°F, Gas 4

4 x 15 cm/6 in squares focaccia (ciabatta) bread

CHICKEN TOPPING
1/2 cup/125 mL/4 fl oz prepared tomato pasta sauce
90 g/3 oz chopped cooked chicken
8 mushrooms, chopped
1 green pepper, chopped
4 spring onions, finely chopped
4 pitted black olives, sliced
60 g/2 oz grated reduced-fat Cheddar cheese
30 g/1 oz grated Parmesan cheese

1 Spread each square of focaccia (ciabatta) with tomato sauce. Top with chicken, mushrooms, green pepper, spring onions and olives. Combine Cheddar and Parmesan cheeses and sprinkle over chicken and vegetables.

2 Place pizzas on nonstick baking trays and bake for 20 minutes or until cheese is melted and golden brown.

2715 kilojoules (645 Calories) per serve
Carbohydrate	96 g (56%)	high
Fat	15 g	medium

Pitta Pizzas, Chicken Pizzas

Pork with Plum Sauce

Serves 4

500 g/1 lb pork fillet, trimmed of all
visible fat
6 spring onions, sliced
2 zucchini (courgettes), sliced
1 red pepper, chopped
2 stalks celery, chopped
250 g/8 oz broccoli florets
freshly ground black pepper
2 cups/440 g/14 oz rice or 500 g/1 lb
noodles, cooked

PLUM SAUCE
2 tablespoons low-salt soy sauce
4 tablespoons plum jam
1/2 cup/125 mL/4 fl oz chicken stock
3 teaspoons cornflour blended
with 1 tablespoon water

1   Cut pork into thin medallions.
Heat a large nonstick frying pan or
wok over a high heat, add pork and
stir-fry for 4-5 minutes or until
browned.

2   Add spring onions, zucchini
(courgettes), red pepper, celery and
broccoli and stir-fry for 3-4 minutes
longer.

3   To make sauce, place soy
sauce, jam and stock in a small
bowl and mix to combine. Stir sauce
into pork mixture and cook, stirring,
for 2-3 minutes or until heated
through. Season to taste with black
pepper and serve with hot rice or
noodles.

2810 kilojoules (670 Calories) per serve
Carbohydrate   102.5 g (60%)   high
Fat   7.5 g   low

Sesame Beef

Serves 4

500 g/1 lb rump steak, trimmed of all
visible fat and cut into strips
3 tablespoons low-salt soy sauce
2 tablespoons honey
1 clove garlic, crushed
1 tablespoon sesame seeds
2 onions, sliced
1 red pepper, sliced
200 g/6 1/2 oz snow peas (mangetout),
trimmed
155 g/5 oz button mushrooms, sliced
2 cups/440 g/14 oz rice or 500 g/1 lb
noodles, cooked

1   Place meat, soy sauce, honey,
garlic and sesame seeds in a bowl,
cover and set aside to marinate for
30 minutes.

2   Drain meat and reserve
marinade. Heat a nonstick frying
pan or wok over a high heat, add
meat and stir-fry for 2-3 minutes.
Remove meat from pan, set aside
and keep warm.

3   Add onions to pan and stir-fry for
2-3 minutes or until tender. Add red
pepper, snow peas (mangetout) and
mushrooms and stir-fry for 2
minutes longer. Return meat to pan,
stir in reserved marinade and cook
for 1 minute. Serve with hot rice or
noodles.

2920 kilojoules (695 Calories) per serve
Carbohydrate   95 g (54%)   medium
Fat   11 g   medium

Mongolian Lamb

Serves 4

500 g/1 lb lamb fillets, trimmed of all
visible fat
2 onions, chopped
2 cups/440 g/14 oz rice or 500 g/1 lb
noodles, cooked

GINGER CHILLI SAUCE
2 tablespoons low-salt soy sauce
1 clove garlic, crushed
1 teaspoon grated fresh ginger
1/2 cup/125 mL/4 fl oz red wine
2 tablespoons sweet chilli sauce

1   Cut lamb into thin medallions.

2   Heat a nonstick frying pan or
wok over a medium-high heat, add
onions and stir-fry for 3-4 minutes or
until golden.

3   Add lamb to pan and stir-fry for
4-5 minutes or until tender.

4   To make sauce, place soy
sauce, garlic, ginger, wine and chilli
sauce in a bowl and mix to
combine. Add sauce to pan and
cook, stirring, for 3-4 minutes or until
sauce thickens. Serve with hot rice
or noodles.

2755 kilojoules (655 Calories) per serve
Carbohydrate   90 g (54%)   medium
Fat   9.5 g   low

Sesame Beef, Mongolian Lamb, Pork with
Plum Sauce

THE TASTE OF FITNESS

Plates In Residence   Cutlery Orrefors Kosta Boda

Spicy Chicken Burgers

Serves 4

1 teaspoon ground cumin
1 teaspoon ground coriander
1 teaspoon paprika
1/4 teaspoon chilli powder
4 boneless chicken breast fillets, skinned
4 rolls, split and lightly toasted
8 lettuce leaves
4 tablespoons low-oil mayonnaise
1/2 avocado, stoned, peeled and chopped

1   Place cumin, coriander, paprika and chilli powder in a bowl and mix to combine. Add chicken to spice mixture and toss to coat.

2   Heat a nonstick frying pan over a high heat, add chicken and cook for 3-4 minutes each side or until tender and cooked through.

3   Top bottom half of each bun with a chicken fillet, 2 lettuce leaves, 1 tablespoon mayonnaise, some of the avocado and top half of bun. Serve immediately.

1300 kilojoules (310 Calories) per serve
Carbohydrate	22 g (28%)	low
Fat	12 g	medium

Steak Sandwiches

Serves 4

4 small pieces rump steak, trimmed of all visible fat
2 onions, sliced
8 thick slices bread, toasted
4 tablespoons barbecue sauce
4 slices reduced-fat Cheddar cheese

1   Heat a nonstick frying pan over a high heat, add steak and cook for 3-4 minutes each side or until cooked to your liking. Remove steak from pan, set aside and keep warm.

2   Add onions to pan and cook, stirring, for 4-5 minutes or until golden and soft.

3   Divide the steak and onions between half the bread slices then top each with 1 tablespoon barbecue sauce, 1 slice cheese and finally a slice of the remaining bread. Serve immediately.

Serving suggestion: Serve Steak Sandwiches with a salad for a complete meal.

1235 kilojoules (295 Calories) per serve
Carbohydrate	35 g (46%)	low
Fat	8 g	low

Soya Burgers

Serves 4

4 rolls, split and toasted
1 carrot, grated
4 slices tomato
1 raw beetroot, peeled and grated (optional)
2-3 tablespoons sweet chilli sauce

SOYA PATTIES
440 g/14 oz canned soya beans, rinsed and drained
125 g/4 oz low-fat cottage cheese
1 cup/60 g/ 2 oz breadcrumbs, made from stale bread
1 teaspoon ground cumin

1   To make patties, place half the soya beans in a bowl and mash with a fork. Add remaining beans, cottage cheese, breadcrumbs and cumin and mix well to combine. Divide bean mixture into four portions and shape into patties.

2   Heat a nonstick frying pan over a medium heat, add patties and cook for 4-6 minutes each side or until brown and heated through.

3   Top bottom half of each roll with a pattie, some carrot, a tomato slice, some beetroot (if using), chilli sauce to taste and top half of roll. Serve immediately.

1355 kilojoules (325 Calories) per serve
Carbohydrate	39 g (47%)	low
Fat	8 g	low

Fish Burgers

Serves 4

4 x 100 g/3 1/2 oz firm white fish fillets
3 tablespoons water
1 tablespoon lemon juice
6 black peppercorns
2 sprigs fresh dill
4 rolls, split and toasted

TARTARE SAUCE
1/2 cup/125 mL/4 fl oz low-oil mayonnaise
2 gherkins, chopped
2 teaspoons chopped fresh dill
freshly ground black pepper

1   To make sauce, place mayonnaise, gherkins, dill and black pepper to taste in a bowl and mix to combine.

2   Place fish, water, lemon juice, peppercorns and dill in a large nonstick frying pan, bring to simmering over a low heat and simmer, turning once, for 3-4 minutes or until fish flakes when tested with a fork. Remove fish from liquid.

3   Top bottom half of each roll with a fish fillet, 1 tablespoon sauce and top half of roll. Serve immediately.

1025 kilojoules (245 Calories) per serve
Carbohydrate	22 g (35%)	low
Fat	4 g	very low

Fish Burger, Soya Burger, Steak Sandwich, Spicy Chicken Burger

CAN YOU KICK THE SALT HABIT?

Salt (sodium chloride) is the main source of sodium in our diet. In countries where salt intake is high, there is an increased rate of high blood pressure, stroke and heart disease.

The body's requirements for salt are low – a mere 0.5 g/day is all that we need. In Western countries the average daily intake is about ten times this amount. Of the salt we eat, 75% comes from processed foods, 15-20% from the salt we add to food and only about 10% from fresh foods such as milk, meat, seafood and fruit.

Sweating increases our salt loss, but the body adapts to reduce the salt content in sweat (and in urine) when large amounts of sweat are lost on a regular basis. Therefore eating extra salt

is not necessary, even for those athletes who sweat heavily.

In longer or ultra-endurance events (greater than 4 hours strenuous, uninterrrupted effort) the body could need extra salt. Large sweat losses occurring in these events increase the chance of blood sodium levels falling, particularly if lots of plain water is used to replace sweat losses. Sodium (salt) losses are best replaced during the event with the help of a fluid-replacement drink containing a low concentration of salt (sodium). There is no need for these athletes to consume extra salt at other times. Salt tablets are not recommended as they may upset the stomach.

EATING TO WIN
COMPETITION EATING

Your dietary needs for competition are dictated by the type of sport you participate in. Read through this guide to competition eating so you will be eating to win.

On Your Mark

Carbohydrate (glycogen) loading

Carbohydrate loading increases the body's store of glycogen. The extra glycogen is loaded to ensure an adequate supply of glycogen for endurance exercise, where normal stores will not be sufficient to maintain stamina. 'Hitting the wall' is an expression used by endurance athletes to describe the feeling they get when glycogen stores are almost exhausted. The 'wall' is a wall of fatigue they feel they cannot pass through.

Earliest loading methods included a glycogen depletion phase. The depletion phase, employed to make the muscles 'hungrier for glycogen' was achieved by strenuous, endurance exercise and severe restriction of carbohydrate intake. Consequently, athletes felt tired, irritable and had difficulty in maintaining motivation and concentration. After 2-3 days of depletion, glycogen was loaded through a diet rich in carbohydrate (9-10 g carbohydrate/kg body weight/day or 80-85% of energy from carbohydrate).

In the 1980s a modified loading method was developed. This method simply involved tapered (reduced) training and a high-carbohydrate diet. The depletion phase was omitted, as similar amounts of glycogen could be loaded without it and the side effects associated with this phase were eliminated.

This modified method is now the only loading method recommended.

Who needs carbohydrate loading?

Carbohydrate loading is only useful for endurance athletes competing in events longer than 90 minutes. In shorter events, an adequate, rather than 'loaded', glycogen store is appropriate. This can be achieved by tapering training and ensuring a high carbohydrate intake (9-10 g carbohydrate/kg body weight/day) 24-36 hours prior to competition.

Low blood sugar (hypoglycaemia)

Endurance exercise places huge demands on the body's carbohydrate reserves. As a result, blood sugar levels may fall too low. Dizziness, shakiness, faintness and confusion are symptoms of hypoglycaemia, or low blood sugar. Athletes may refer to this as 'bonking'.

Adequate preparation for endurance events through carbohydrate loading and the replacement of carbohydrate during the event with diluted (5-10% carbohydrate) sports drinks or food snacks help to prevent this problem.

Loading tips

▸ Taper (reduce) training to decrease the use of muscle glycogen. This is also important to help you peak. Rest on the day prior to competition. Cramming in extra training this close to competiton does more harm than good.

▸ Eat extra carbohydrate for 3-4 days prior to the event. Aim to consume approximately 9-10 g of carbohydrate/kg of body weight/day (see pages 19 and 20).

▸ If feeling full or bloated, try reducing fibre intake. Choose white bread, rice or pasta and more refined cereals such as Cornflakes or Rice Bubbles, instead of the higher fibre, wholegrain ones. Resume a high-fibre diet after competition.

▸ If you can't manage to eat the amount of food you need, juices, soft drinks and high-carbohydrate sports drinks help to supplement food intake.

▸ Check your body weight. Approximately 3 g of water are stored with each gram of loaded glycogen. Expect to gain about 2 kg/ 4 lb. The water stored assists hydration during the event.

Precompetition meal

Your precompetition meal has the potential to either make or break your performance on the day. What you will be eating should not be left to chance. Work on a dietary strategy using the following guidelines, then practise this strategy before a training session so you can fine tune your diet.

PRECOMPETITION MEAL GUIDELINES

▸ High in carbohydrate – for maximum energy

▸ Low in fat – fat slows digestion

▸ Moderate protein – fill up on carbohydrates instead

▸ Avoid salty foods and added salt – salt (and protein) has a diuretic (dehydrating) effect

▸ Avoid caffeine and alcohol – they have a diuretic effect

▸ Moderate fibre – not too much of a good thing (see page 31)

▸ Top up, don't pig out – eat a comfortable amount of food

▸ Drink your meal – if you're too nervous, or you feel it's too early in the morning to eat, try a sports drink, or see drinks recipes (page 33). Maintain your energy with liquid food

▸ Practise – experiment with different meals to find out which foods work best for you

The Precompetition Meal

There is no perfect precompetition meal. Use these guidelines to develop your own precompetition meal plan, based around the foods you enjoy.

GOOD BREAKFAST

Wholegrain cereal (pictured, Kellogg's Sustain) with reduced-fat milk
Fresh fruit
2 slices toast spread with jam (no butter or margarine)
1 glass pure fruit juice (100%)

Nutritional Analysis

Energy	2100 kJ (500 Cal)
Protein	12 g (10%)
Fat	4 g (5 %)
Carbohydrate	100 g (85%)

▶ *Cereal, bread, fruit and fruit juice are high in carbohydrate and low in fat.*

NOT RECOMMENDED BREAKFAST

1 fried egg
2 rashers bacon with fat
1 beef sausage
2 thick slices white toast spread thickly with butter
1 cup black coffee, no sugar

Nutritional Analysis

Energy	2100 kJ (500 Cal)
Protein	30 g (23%)
Fat	33 g (50%)
Carbohydrate	30 g (27%)

▶ *The egg, bacon and sausage fry-up is high in fat.*
▶ *The meal is low in carbohydrate.*
▶ *The caffeine in the coffee has a diuretic (dehydrating) effect.*

GOOD DINNER

White spaghetti, topped with tomato-based sauce (prepared without fat or oil)
1 large white bread roll (no butter or margarine)
Fresh fruit
1 glass orange juice (100%)

Nutritional Analysis

Energy	4300 kJ (1000 Cal)
Protein	33 g (14%)
Fat	7 g (6%)
Carbohydrate	200 g (80%)

▶ *Pasta, bread, fruit and fruit juice are all low in fat and high in carbohydrate.*
▶ *Small amounts of meat, fish or chicken can be added to the sauce if desired.*

NOT RECOMMENDED DINNER

Rump steak fried with fat
1 baked jacket potato
Green salad
Garlic bread, spread thickly with butter
2 scoops vanilla ice cream

Nutritional Analysis

Energy	4240 kJ (1000 Cal)
Protein	71 g (29%)
Fat	57 g (50%)
Carbohydrate	55 g (21%)

▶ *Carbohydrate content is too low.*
▶ *Fat on meat, in garlic butter on bread and in ice cream results in a meal too high in fat.*

Precompetition proportions

You should aim for the following when planning your precompetition meal.
Fat – less than 20% of energy (less than 10 g fat/meal)
Carbohydrate – about 80-85% of energy
Compare the precompetition 'good' and 'bad' breakfasts and dinners and see how they rate.

Get Set

The meal immediately prior to the event, the precompetition meal, is like the 'icing on the cake'. This one meal can't work miracles if the diet leading up to competition has been inadequate. However, this one meal could break your performance if the wrong foods are eaten.

'When should I eat my precompetition meal?'

You will feel more comfortable if you eat your precompetition meal 2-4 hours prior to the event. This allows time for the meal to be emptied from the stomach. Allow 4 hours for a larger meal.

'I compete in a series of heats/ sessions throughout the day. What should I eat in between?'

Eat small amounts regularly throughout the day. You will feel more comfortable if you are not over full. In shorter breaks (less than 1 hour) drinks are best; try either water or a fluid-replacement drink. In longer breaks, try a light snack (see box above) or a fruit drink or reduced-fat milk drink. Refuelling with a drink between events aids rehydration and is often more comfortable and convenient than food.

'If I eat well the evening before the event, do I still need to eat breakfast?'

Yes, you do! Liver glycogen stores fall overnight. While you sleep, your liver uses its stores of glycogen to top up blood sugar levels. If these stores are not replaced prior to the event, your concentration levels may slide, you may even feel dizzy or sleepy during competition. To compete at your maximum, both liver and muscle glycogen stores need to be at their best. Fruit sugar, fructose, is taken up quickly by the liver so it's good to include some fruit or juice in your precompetition breakfast. A homemade (see page 33) or commercially available liquid meal, such as Exceed Sports Nutrition Supplement or Sustagen, is fine if eating solid food prior to the event is difficult for you.

MEAL IDEAS

Pre-event

◗ Breakfast cereal with reduced-fat milk and fresh, canned or dried fruit

◗ Pancakes with honey, jam or maple syrup

◗ English muffins, crumpets or bread/toast topped with jam, honey, banana, baked beans or spaghetti

◗ Pasta with tomato or low-fat sauce

◗ Homemade liquid meals (page 33) or commercial varieties, such as Exceed Sports Nutrition Supplement or Sustagen

Between Events

As for pre-event, plus:

◗ Quick Banana Rice Custard (page 16). This is delicious cold

◗ Cheese and Chive Scones (page 13)

◗ Muffins (page 13)

◗ Muesli Bars (page 13)

◗ Pikelets (page 16)

◗ Banana sandwich

◗ Honey or jam sandwich

◗ Fruit Bread Pudding (page 66)

◗ Sandwiches

◗ Exceed Sports or Power bars

◗ Low-fat yogurt

◗ Fresh, canned or dried fruit

'I get a bloated or upset stomach if I eat before I compete – what foods should I try?'

Use the guidelines on this page and the pre-event meal ideas (page 60) as a starting point. If you get no relief, try a liquid meal as these are well tolerated even by those who have a 'nervous' or sensitive stomach, prior to an event. Liquid meals are also low in fibre so they help to prevent excessive bowel movement before or during the event. See also 'Fibre – too much of a good thing?' (page 31).

Go

During the event, fluid replacement is vital for everyone. Refuelling with carbohydrate along the way will benefit endurance athletes, particularly if the events are longer than 2 hours. See the section on fluids and refuelling (page 34). Don't forget your recovery strategies after the event (see page 21).

3-DAY PRECOMPETITON MENU PLAN

Menu plan explained

Each daily menu provides approximately 14 700 kilojoules (3500 Calories). Of this, 10 500 kilojoules (3000 Calories) comes from meals and the remainder from snacks. The energy (kilojoule/calorie) level is suitable for active males. For females and those less active, smaller servings and reducing or omitting some of the snacks will help to decrease the energy to the appropriate level. Alternatively, increasing foods such as bread, fruit, juice, rice and pasta will increase the energy and carbohydrate in the daily menu.

The proportion of energy from protein, fat and carbohydrate is approximately 20% protein, 10% fat and 70% carbohydrate. This plan will give you ideas on how to organise your own high-carbohydrate, low-fat menu plans using other foods and recipes from this book.

DAY 1

BREAKFAST
1 piece fresh fruit
Banana Porridge (page 9) with reduced-fat milk
2 slices bread or toast spread with jam, honey or marmalade
1 small glass fruit juice

Morning Snack
Mango Smoothie (page 33)

LUNCH
3 sandwiches or bread rolls (see page 25 for Delicious Sandwich Fillings)
2 pieces fresh fruit
1 small glass fruit juice

Afternoon Snack
Honey Soy Noodles (page 14)

DINNER
Curry Lamb Stir-Fry (page 45) served with rice and either steamed vegetables or a salad (no-oil dressing)
2 pieces fresh fruit
1 small glass fruit juice

Supper
1 piece fresh fruit
2 slices raisin bread spread with jam, honey or marmalade
1 small glass fruit juice

DAY 2

BREAKFAST
1 piece fresh fruit
1 large bowl Kellogg's Sustain with reduced-fat milk
2 slices bread or toast spread with jam, honey or marmalade
1 glass reduced-fat milk

Morning Snack
1 piece fresh fruit

LUNCH
Spinach and Pasta Salad (page 22)
1 piece fresh fruit
1 small glass fruit juice

Afternoon Snack
1 Banana Muffin (page 13)
1 small glass fruit juice

DINNER
Pork with Plum Sauce (page 56) served with rice or noodles and extra steamed vegetables or a salad (no-oil dressing)
2 slices bread or a bread roll
1 piece fresh fruit
1 Pineapple Crush (page 33)

Supper
2 crumpets spread with jam or honey
1 small glass reduced-fat milk

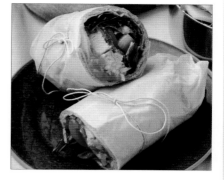

DAY 3

BREAKFAST
3 pieces fresh fruit, chopped and served with 1 carton (200 g/6½ oz) low-fat fruit yogurt
2 Pancakes (page 70)
1 small glass fruit juice

Morning Snack
1 Muesli Bar (page 13)
1 small glass fruit juice

LUNCH
1 Chicken Satay Roll-Up (page 26)
1 piece fresh fruit
1 Powershake (page 33)

Afternoon Snack
1 piece fresh fruit
1 small glass fruit juice

DINNER
Pasta with Tomato Chilli and Herb Sauce (page 40)
2 slices bread or a bread roll
Quick Fruit Bread Pudding (page 66)
1 small glass fruit juice

Supper
1 large bowl wholegrain cereal with reduced-fat milk
1 piece fresh fruit

SWEET TREATS
SPECIAL REWARDS

Carrot Cake with Lemon Frosting

Serves 12
Oven temp: 180°C, 350°F, Gas 4

1 cup/125 g/4 oz flour
1 teaspoon baking powder
1/2 teaspoon bicarbonate of soda
3/4 cup/125 g/4 oz brown sugar
1 carrot, grated
1/2 cup/90 g/3 oz chopped canned pineapple, drained
2 eggs
2 tablespoons vegetable oil
1 teaspoon ground cinnamon

LEMON FROSTING
125 g/4 oz low-fat ricotta cheese
1/4 cup/45 g/11/2 oz icing sugar
1 tablespoon lemon juice

1   Sift together flour, baking powder and bicarbonate of soda into a bowl, add sugar and mix to combine.

2   Add carrot, pineapple, eggs, oil and cinnamon and mix well.

3   Spoon batter into an 18 cm/7 in round cake tin lined with nonstick baking paper and bake for 35-40 minutes or until cooked when tested with a skewer. Allow cake to stand in tin for 5 minutes before turning onto a wire rack to cool completely.

4   To make frosting, place ricotta cheese, icing sugar and lemon juice in a food processor and process until smooth. Spread over the top of cold cake.

625 kilojoules (150 Calories) per slice

Carbohydrate	*23 g (60%)*	*high*
Fat	*5 g*	*low*

Chocolate Brownies

Makes 16 squares
Oven temp: 180°C, 350°F, Gas 4

3/4 cup/90 g/3 oz flour
1/2 teaspoon baking powder
1/2 cup/45 g/11/2 oz cocoa powder
1 cup/ 220 g/7 oz caster sugar
1/2 cup/100 g/3 oz low-fat vanilla yogurt
2 eggs
1 teaspoon vanilla essence
11/2 tablespoons vegetable oil

1   Sift together flour, baking powder and cocoa powder into a bowl. Add sugar, yogurt, eggs, vanilla essence and oil and mix to combine.

2   Spoon batter into a 20 cm/8 in square cake tin lined with nonstick baking paper and bake for 25-30 minutes. Allow brownies to cool in tin before turning out and cutting into squares.

Cook's tip: If you do not have a nonstick baking tin, line tin with nonstick baking paper.

500 kilojoules (120 Calories) per brownie

Carbohydrate	*21 g (68%)*	*high*
Fat	*3 g*	*very low*

Carrot Cake with Lemon Frosting, Brownies

Blue Plate Inner City Clayworkers Gallery   Orange Plate Limoges   Basket Basic Essentials   Napkin In Residence

Quick Fruit Bread Pudding

Serves 6
Oven temp: 180°C, 350°F, Gas 4

8 slices fruit bread
2 tablespoons jam
3 eggs
2¼ cups/600 mL/1 pt skim milk

1   Trim crusts from bread and cut slices into triangles. Spread each triangle with a little jam and arrange in a 6 cup/1.5 litre/2½ pt capacity ovenproof dish.

2   Place eggs and milk in a bowl and whisk to combine. Pour milk mixture over bread and bake for 35-40 minutes or until custard is set and top is golden.

Serving suggestion: This dessert is delicious served with low-fat ice cream or low-fat vanilla yogurt.

845 kilojoules (200 Calories) per serve
Carbohydrate   31.5 g (61%)   high
Fat   4 g   very low

Fruit with Strawberry Dip

Serves 4

200 g/6½ oz vanilla *fromage frais*
200 g/6½ oz strawberries
fresh fruit of your choice

Place strawberries in a food processor or blender and process to make a purée. Place strawberry purée in a bowl, add *fromage frais* and mix to combine. Serve with fruit.

225 kilojoules (55 Calories) per serve of dip
Carbohydrate   7.5 g (55%)   medium
Fat   1 g   very low

White Dish Country Road   White Plate Limoges   Blue Plate Lifestyle Imports

Mango Cheesecake

Serves 12
Oven temp: 180°C, 350°F, Gas 4

BASE
8 Weet-Bix (Weetabix), crushed
2 tablespoons honey
2 tablespoons orange juice

MANGO FILLING
1½ cups/300 g/10 oz low-fat vanilla yogurt
500 g/1 lb low-fat ricotta cheese
¼ cup/60 mL/2 fl oz lemon juice
½ cup/100 g/3½ oz caster sugar
4 egg whites
2 x 440 g/14 oz canned mango slices, drained

1   To make base, place Weet-Bix (Weetabix), honey and orange juice in a bowl and mix well to combine. Press base into a 23 cm/9 in springform tin lined with nonstick baking paper and bake for 10 minutes.

2   To make filling, place yogurt, ricotta cheese, lemon juice, sugar, egg whites and half the mango slices in a food processor and process until smooth. Roughly chop remaining mango slices and fold into filling.

3   Spoon filling over base and bake for 35-45 minutes or until set. Refrigerate until well chilled before serving.

830 kilojoules (200 Calories) per serve

Carbohydrate	*33 g (65%)*	*high*
Fat	*4 g*	*very low*

Mango Cheesecake, Quick Fruit Bread Pudding, Fruit with Strawberry Dip

Pumpkin Fruit Cake

Serves 12
Oven temp: 180°C, 350°F, Gas 4

¹/₂ cup/60 g/2 oz self-raising flour
1 cup/125 g/4 oz flour
¹/₂ cup/125 g/4 oz demerara sugar
155 g/5 oz mixed dried fruit
1 cup/250 g/8 oz cooked mashed pumpkin
1 egg
¹/₂ cup/100 g/3¹/₂ oz low-fat natural yogurt
1 teaspoon vanilla essence

1   Sift together self-raising flour and flour in a bowl, add sugar and dried fruit and mix to combine.

2   Make a well in the centre of the flour mixture, add pumpkin, egg, yogurt and vanilla essence and mix to combine.

3   Spoon batter into a 20 cm/8 in square cake tin lined with nonstick baking paper and bake for 50-60 minutes or until cake is cooked when tested with a skewer.

615 kilojoules (145 Calories) per slice

Carbohydrate	32 g (85%)	very high
Fat	1 g	very low

Apricot Bran Loaf

Serves 12
Oven temp: 180°C, 350°F, Gas 4

60 g/2 oz chopped dried apricots
¹/₄ cup/60 mL/2 fl oz hot water
¹/₂ cup/75 g/2¹/₂ oz wholemeal flour
1 cup/125 g/4 oz self-raising flour
1 teaspoon baking powder
1 cup/100 g/3¹/₂ oz bran cereal
2 eggs
¹/₄ cup/45 g/1¹/₂ oz low-fat natural yogurt
¹/₂ cup/170 g/5¹/₂ oz honey
1 teaspoon ground allspice

1   Place apricots in a bowl, pour over hot water and set aside to soak for 15 minutes.

2   Sift together wholemeal flour, self-raising flour and baking powder and return husks to bowl. Add bran cereal and mix to combine. Stir in eggs, yogurt, honey, allspice and apricot mixture and mix well.

3   Spoon batter into an 11 x 21 cm/ 4¹/₂ x 8¹/₂ in loaf tin lined with nonstick baking paper and bake for 45 minutes or until cooked when tested with a skewer.

600 kilojoules (145 Calories) per slice

Carbohydrate	29 g (80%)	very high
Fat	1 g	very low

Oaty Orange Biscuits

Makes 16
Oven temp: 180°C, 350°F, Gas 4

¹/₂ cup/170 g/5¹/₂ oz honey
¹/₂ cup/125 mL/4 fl oz orange juice
1 cup/90 g/3 oz rolled oats
1 cup/125 g/4 oz flour, sifted
¹/₂ cup 125 g/4 oz sugar
1 tablespoon finely grated orange rind
1 teaspoon bicarbonate of soda
2 tablespoons boiling water

1   Place honey and orange juice in a small saucepan, bring to simmering over a medium heat and simmer, stirring occasionally, for 8-10 minutes or until mixture is thick and syrupy.

2   Place oats, flour, sugar and orange rind in a bowl and mix to combine. Add honey mixture to oats mixture and mix well.

3   Combine bicarbonate of soda with water and stir into oats mixture.

4   Shape tablespoons of mixture into balls, place on a baking tray lined with nonstick baking paper and bake for 10-12 minutes or until golden. Allow biscuits to cool on trays for 5 minutes before removing to a wire rack to cool completely.

470 kilojoules (115 Calories) per biscuit

Carbohydrate	26 g (90%)	very high
Fat	0.5 g	very low

Apricot Bran Loaf, Pumpkin Fruit Cake, Oaty Orange Biscuits

Plates Inner City Clayworkers Gallery

Pancakes

Makes 12 pancakes
Serves 6

1½ cups/185 g/6 oz self-raising flour
½ teaspoon baking powder
⅓ cup/75 g/2½ oz caster sugar
2 eggs lightly beaten
1½ cups/375 mL/12 fl oz reduced-fat milk or buttermilk

1　Sift together flour and baking powder into a bowl, add sugar and mix to combine. Add eggs and milk and mix until smooth.

2　Heat a nonstick frying pan over a medium heat, pour 3 tablespoons of batter into pan and cook for 1 minute each side or until golden. Remove pancake, set aside and keep warm. Repeat with remaining batter. Serve pancakes hot with honey or maple syrup.

990 kilojoules (235 Calories) per serve

Carbohydrate	45 g (75%)	very high
Fat	3 g	very low

Strawberry Sponge

Serves 12
Oven temp: 180°C, 350°F, Gas 4

SPONGE
3 eggs
½ cup/100 g/3½ oz caster sugar
¼ cup/30 g/1 oz cornflour
¼ cup/30 g/1 oz flour
¼ cup/30 g/1 oz self-raising flour

STRAWBERRY FILLING
250 g/8 oz strawberries, hulled and halved
200 g/6½ oz strawberry *fromage frais*
icing sugar

1　To make Sponge, place eggs in a bowl and beat with an electric mixer for 5 minutes or until light and fluffy. Gradually add sugar, beating well after each addition until mixture is thick and creamy.

2　Sift together cornflour, flour and self-raising flour.

3　Fold flour mixture into egg mixture. Pour batter into two 18 cm/ 7 in round cake tins lined with nonstick baking paper and bake for 15 minutes or until cake springs back when lightly pressed with fingertips.

4　Turn cakes onto wire racks to cool. Spread one cake with *fromage frais* and top with strawberries. Place remaining cake on top, sprinkle with icing sugar and decorate with extra strawberries, if desired.

420 kilojoules (100 Calories) per slice

Carbohydrate	18.5 g (72%)	very high
Fat	1.5 g	very low

Right: Strawberry Sponge
Below: Pancakes

FREEZE IT

MEALS IN A FLASH

One of the easiest ways to provide quick meals is to cook ahead and freeze. Freezing meals successfully is simple but does require a little thought and planning.

The following tips will ensure successful results:

▶ Cold air is drying, so food for freezing should be packaged in airtight and moisture-proof containers.

▶ Foil and plastic containers are ideal for freezing.

▶ Clear labelling is essential when freezing. Be sure to label packages to be frozen clearly with the date and contents. Remember frozen food looks very different from fresh food and in a week, month or year you may not know what is in the packet or how long it has been there.

▶ Freezer bags made of heavy transparent polythene are ideal. These are great for packing vegetables, meat, chicken, fish and irregular-shaped foods. When using freezer bags, squeeze out as much air as possible before sealing with twist ties or freezer tape.

2-3 minutes or until onion is soft. Add broccoli, zucchini (courgettes) and green pepper and cook, stirring, for 3-4 minutes or until just tender. Add pasta sauce and cook, stirring, for 3-4 minutes or until heated through. Add tuna and mix to combine. Set aside.

2 To make Cheese Sauce, place ricotta and Parmesan cheeses in a bowl and mix to combine. Stir in enough milk to make a smooth sauce of spreading consistency.

3 Place 1½ sheets of lasagne in the base of four foil containers, top with one-quarter of the Tomato Tuna Sauce and 1 tablespoon of the Cheese Sauce. Repeat layers until all ingredients are used. Sprinkle with Cheddar cheese and bake for 30-35 minutes or until lasagne sheets are soft. Remove lasagne from oven and set aside to cool.

When cold, place lids on foil containers, seal, label and freeze.

To reheat: Thaw in the refrigerator or defrost in the microwave. Reheat in the oven at 180°C/350°F/Gas 4 for 20 minutes or in the microwave on MEDIUM (50%) for 10 minutes or until heated through.

2715 kilojoules (645 Calories) per slice

Carbohydrate	75 g (45%)	low
Fat	15 g	medium

Cook's tip: Foil containers can be used in the microwave providing you remember the following rules:

▶ Never let metal touch metal. So do not allow the foil container to touch the sides of the microwave and, if you have a metal turntable, place the container on a nonmetal rack.

▶ Have more food exposed than metal. Containers should be no more than 3-4 cm/1½-1¾ in deep and always microwave with the lid removed or cover the container with microwave-safe plastic food wrap.

Individual Tuna Lasagne

Serves 4
Oven temp: 180°C, 350°F, Gas 4

16 sheets instant lasagne
60 g/2 oz grated reduced-fat Cheddar cheese

TOMATO TUNA SAUCE

1 onion, chopped
1 clove garlic, crushed
125 g/4 oz broccoli florets
2 zucchini (courgettes), chopped
1 green pepper, chopped
500 mL/16 fl oz jar prepared tomato pasta sauce
440 g/14 oz canned tuna in springwater, drained

CHEESE SAUCE

155 g/5 oz low-fat ricotta cheese
4 tablespoons grated Parmesan cheese
2-3 tablespoons reduced-fat milk

1 To make Tomato Tuna Sauce, cook onion and garlic in a nonstick frying pan over a medium heat for

Individual Tuna Lasagne, Steamed Jam Pudding with Microwave Custard

MICROWAVE IT

WHEN TIME IS SHORT

Microwaving saves you time preparing and reheating meals. Use the following tips and recipes to help you master your microwave.

Even cooking: Arrange food so that the thicker portions are on the outside of the turntable and the thinner portions towards the centre. When arranged in this way you will find that the food cooks more evenly. For even-shaped pieces of food you will need to rearrange them during cooking.

Aluminium foil: Uneven portions of meat will overcook on the thinner areas. This can be prevented by shielding these areas with small strips of foil. Covering the corners of square or oblong dishes with foil will prevent these areas from overcooking.

Covering: Generally food that requires covering for conventional cooking will also need to be covered for microwaving. Most food requires covering when reheating. Be sure to use a good quality microwave-safe plastic food wrap for covering dishes that do not have lids.

Defrosting: Pack meat or chicken in single layers for freezing. Thaw in the microwave on DEFROST (30%). You will find that the outside portions defrost more quickly than those in the centre. Remove food as it thaws.

Steamed Jam Puddings

Serves 4

15 g/¹/₂ oz polyunsaturated margarine
¹/₄ cup/60 g/2 oz low-fat natural yogurt
¹/₄ cup/60 g/2 oz sugar
1 egg
1 teaspoon vanilla essence
³/₄ cup/90 g/3 oz self-raising flour, sifted
1-1¹/₂ tablespoons reduced-fat milk
4 tablespoons berry jam of your choice

1   Place margarine in a microwave-safe bowl and soften in the microwave on MEDIUM (50%) for 30 seconds.

2   Add yogurt and sugar to margarine and mix to combine. Beat in egg, vanilla essence, flour and milk and mix until smooth.

3   Place 1 tablespoon of jam in the base of four microwave-safe teacups. Divide batter evenly between cups and cover with microwave-safe plastic food wrap.

4   Cook puddings, elevated, on HIGH (100%) for 2-3 minutes. Stand for 3-4 minutes before removing wrap. To serve, invert puddings onto serving plates and serve with Microwave Custard.

1080 kilojoules (250 Calories) per slice
Carbohydrate   50 g (75%)   very high
Fat   5 g   low

Microwave Custard

Makes 1¹/₂ cups/375 mL/12 fl oz

2 tablespoons sugar
3 tablespoons custard powder
1 teaspoon vanilla essence
1¹/₂ cups/375 mL/12 fl oz reduced-fat milk

1   Place sugar, custard, vanilla and a little milk in a large microwave-safe jar and mix to a smooth paste.

2   Stir in remaining milk and cook on HIGH (100%), stirring after 2 minutes, for 4-5 minutes or until custard boils and thickens.

475 kilojoules (115 Calories) per ¹/₂ cup/125mL/ 4 fl oz
Carbohydrate   16 g (53%)   medium
Fat   3.5 g   very low

DIETING
ARE YOU OBSESSED?

For some people, especially women, dieting is a way of life. Gaining only a few grams can depress them for the day.

A dinner out ruins their diet routine. Food can no longer be enjoyed because for them it is surrounded by guilt. With society's pre-occupation with slimness, obsessive dieting is on the increase. Are you obsessed? See how you rate in the Diet Quiz.

Are you really overweight?

The fashionable body weight changes, along with hairstyles and the length of women's skirts. Marilyn Monroe would be considered fat by today's modelling agencies, as 1990s models are underweight by health standards. Therefore women whose weight is normal and healthy feel overweight next to today's models.

The relationship of your weight to your height is a starting point, but active people need to understand that they may be classified as overweight by a Body Mass Index (BMI) – even though they are not overfat. This is especially the case when there is a higher degree of muscular development as muscle is heavier than fat. Work out your BMI, then read on about better ways to measure fatness. To work out your BMI divide your weight in kilograms by the square of your height in metres.

$$\frac{\text{weight (kg)}}{\text{height}^2 \text{ (metres)}} = \text{BMI}$$

For example, if you weigh 70 kg and your height is 1.75 m

$$\frac{70 \text{ kg}}{1.75^2} = 22.86 \text{ BMI}$$

BMI
less than 20   – underweight
20-25   – healthy weight
25-30   – overweight
greater than 30 – obese

Shaping Up

Many people have a love-hate relationship with their bathroom scales. They may hate weighing themselves, but they can't resist the temptation to step on those scales.

Scales are a poor indicator of fatness for active people. Weight fluctuations can be related to changes in muscle, water or glycogen, but unfortunately we are conditioned to believe they are always fat related.

Better ways to assess fatness include:

The pinch test (skinfold measurements): Fat is pinched with skinfold callipers on various areas of the body to determine the level of body fat. This method is most useful if a skilled person takes a series of measurements over time to track progress.

Circumference measures: If you are a little too overweight for callipers, circumference measurements of your waist, hips, thighs and other parts of your body can be a better indicator of fat loss than the scales, especially if you are exercising and increasing your muscle weight.

ENERGY

All kilojoules (calories) are not equal. Protein, fat, carbo-hydrate and alcohol are the nutrients which provide energy (kilojoules/calories). Fat (37 kJ or 9 Cal/g) and alcohol (29 kJ or 7 Cal/g) provide more kilojoules/calories per gram, than either protein or carbohydrate (16 kJ or 4 Cal/g). Fat is also more easily stored as body fat when compared with protein or carbohydrate. Recent research suggests that alcohol reduces the body's ability to burn up excess fat after a fatty meal.

DIET QUIZ

Do You?	Yes	No
1 Diet even though you don't really need to lose weight (see this page).	☐	☐
2 Feel afraid to change your daily routine because you may gain weight.	☐	☐
3 Get comments from friends and family about how little you eat.	☐	☐
4 Feel guilty when you occasionally eat high-kilojoule/calorie food.	☐	☐
5 Weigh yourself daily and plan your food intake and exercise accordingly.	☐	☐
6 Count up every kilojoule (calorie) you eat.	☐	☐
7 Avoid social occasions based around food.	☐	☐
8 Worry about weight gain if you miss an exercise session.	☐	☐

Scoring: If you answer YES to most of these questions, dieting may be your obsession. Read on to find out more about the down side of dieting.

Body fat – how low can you go?

Elite athletes strive to obtain low body-fat levels for competitive reasons. While the performance benefits cannot be denied for sports such as triathlon, swimming and marathon running, sometimes athletes become obsessed with a particular fat level where even a few extra millimetres seem devastating.

Low body-fat levels may be a breeze for some, yet others struggle to get anywhere near the 'ideal' level touted by the coach, team-mates or self-taught 'experts' – you know the ones I mean. Our body type is genetically determined, so there are limits to our capacity for leanness.

When an athlete's physique is not suited to a particular sport, coaches, parents and, ultimately, the athlete, need to make mature, informed and responsible decisions about methods used to manage physique-related problems. The aftermath of numerous failed dieting attempts can be devastating to both physical and mental health. If sensible approaches are unsuccessful, selecting a sport more suited to the athlete's natural physique characteristics will enable them to compete safely and develop to their full potential. Athletes such as gymnasts, ballet dancers and figure skaters, who need to be careful with their weight and food intake over a prolonged period, may benefit from a daily multi-vitamin supplement as an extra assurance that they obtain an adequate vitamin and mineral intake. Supplements however do not replace the need for a well-balanced diet.

The Yo-Yo Syndrome

Rapid and frequent weight loss and regain, known as the Yo-Yo Syndrome, is a common experience for dieters. Experts suspect that these constant weight fluctuations are the cause of longer term weight-control difficulties.

Crash weight loss reduces muscle. Weight regain is mostly fat. Little by little, with each weight-loss cycle, muscle mass is eroded away while fat mass grows with each weight regain. With less muscle, metabolism is slower. Yo-Yo dieters, systematically use dieting to slow metabolism and make it easier for their bodies to get fatter. A sensible diet and exercise plan is their only rescue. Regular exercise helps to burn up excess fat and rebuild muscle. A sensible diet provides enough fuel for the body to maintain metabolism and for it to exercise energetically, so that dieters can get off this weight-loss roller coaster for good.

Diet check: Put your favourite weight-loss diet to the test. Use the quiz on page 6 to test how balanced the diet is. The results may surprise you.

Cellulite

Cellulite is just fat – not a build-up of 'toxic waste' as you may have been led to believe. The dimply appearance is due to the fat being deposited in the leg and buttock area where connective tissue is laid down between the pockets of fat. As women have thinner skin and tend to lay down fat in this area more than men, they are more likely to have cellulite.

Excess fat in the thigh/buttock area may be unfashionable, but it has a relatively low health risk – unlike excess fat on the belly which increases the risk for heart disease, diabetes and high blood pressure. Loss of leg/buttock fat is more difficult, however, as the fat cells are more resistant. In women, the body is thought to be protective of this fat as it is used as an energy reserve to support pregnancy and breast-feeding, should that occur.

The way to lose cellulite is the same as losing fat anywhere else – sensible eating and regular aerobic exercise. Toning exercises will not help to burn fat, but will help to firm up the leg muscles to improve the overall shape.

> ## DID YOU KNOW?
> Your resting metabolic rate – the amount of fuel your body uses up at rest – is related to the amount of muscle you have. The greater the amount of muscle, the faster the metabolic rate. Fad diets lower muscle mass and your metabolism. Read the Yo-Yo Syndrome to see how incorrect dieting can actually make you fatter!

ON THE ROAD
EATING AWAY FROM HOME

One of the fringe benefits of sport is that it may open up opportunities to travel. You might start off at the next suburb but, if you get lucky, you could be off to distant, interesting places.

Food won't be the same as it is at home, so some knowledge of the typical foods eaten, the food arrangements (especially if travelling in a team), cooking facilities and the like will help you to maintain your dietary goals while you are away.

Be Prepared

The following list of questions should help you to obtain the sort of information you need to know:

1   Will food be provided or will I need to buy my own? (Important to know for your travel budget.)

2   If food is provided, what will it be? Can I buy some extras if I need to?

3   What are the best high-carbohydrate options and what high-fat dishes should I avoid ?

4   Will special airline meals be organised? If not, organise one for yourself – ask for a low-fat or vegetarian meal if special meals for athletes are not available. Stay well hydrated, drink plenty of water and avoid alcoholic or caffeine-containing drinks.

5   Is the water safe to drink? If not, drink boiled or bottled water and avoid ice, raw vegetables (washed in water) and edible skin on fruit. Avoid food at street stalls – choose reputable restaurants instead. Check if dairy products are pasteurised.

Food poisoning can really wipe out your chances of success. If you are in doubt – get some advice from a sports dietitian who can help you to plan your nutrition strategies for travelling and competition.

As you have less control over your food, it's a good idea to take a multi-vitamin supplement each day to ensure that your vitamin and mineral intake is adequate while you're away. Take your favourite sports drinks with you, as they may not be available overseas.

At the Event

Sporting venues have food outlets designed to feed spectators, not athletes. If you are going to eat well you will need to take your own food. See the section on snacks (page 13) and eating between events (page 60) for more ideas. Sports drinks are a good item to keep in your sports bag, as are non-perishable items such as breakfast cereal, instant noodles, dried fruit, water crackers, canned fruit, fruit juice and sports drinks.

Hint for Coaches

For large groups, call a local restaurant ahead of time and organise a healthy meal for when the team is due to arrive. This will speed up service and will ensure your athletes eat well. The fact that you bothered indicates to your athletes that you take seriously the need to eat well.

SUPPLEMENTS
A CONTINUING CONTROVERSY

In the pursuit of the ultimate sports performance, nutrition supplements may be used because they are believed to provide the nutritonal edge. But what do we really know about them? Here is the lowdown on just a few.

Bee Pollen

Proposed use: To provide essential vitamins and minerals which enhance athletic ability.
Scientific research: Shows it contains some essential nutrients but in quantities too small to be significant. Scientific trials have failed to demonstrate benefits to athletic performance.

Carnitine

Proposed use: To assist the transport of fatty acids into the parts of cells which handle energy production.
Claimed to assist fat burning and decrease the production of lactic acid. Also claimed to spare muscle glycogen by increasing the use of fat as a fuel – aimed at delaying fatigue in endurance events.
Scientific research: Earlier studies have shown conflicting results, but more recent studies show no benefit of supplementation on athletic performance.

Co-enzyme Q10

Proposed use: To assist with aerobic metabolism.
Scientific research: Well-designed scientific studies have demonstrated no beneficial effects from Co-enzyme Q10 supplementation in athletes.

Inosine

Proposed use: To assist endurance performance by enhancing energy production. Also to facilitate oxygen release to the muscles via its effect on red blood cell biochemistry.
Scientific research: Limited research does not support claims.

Ginseng

Proposed use: There are numerous claims regarding its potential benefits to performance and general health.
Scientific research: There has been little well-controlled research for ginseng. Studies have been hampered by a lack of consistency in the composition of different ginseng supplements.
The scientific evidence to date fails to support a performance benefit from supplementation.

Caffeine

Proposed use: To enhance endurance via its ability to increase the release of free fatty acids with sparing of muscle glycogen. Also claimed to be a psychological stimulant – used for mental arousal.
Scientific research: Research in the endurance area is conflicting and to date there is no real consensus of opinion as to whether caffeine benefits performance.
Performance benefits related to the stimulant effects seem to be dependent on the individual.
On the down side are the diuretic (dehydrating) properties of caffeine and the possible uncomfortable/ jittery response some people may experience after taking caffeine.
Athletes need to remember that caffeine is a substance which is subject to drug testing. You would need to drink 6-8 cups of coffee or 10 cans of cola drink to exceed the legal limit.

Vitamins and Minerals

Vitamins and minerals are the most popular supplements of all.
Scientific research does not support their use to enhance performance in well-nourished athletes. However, a case can be made for the use of vitamin/mineral supplements in the following situations.
Travelling: It may be difficult to keep to your optimal diet while travelling. A multi-vitamin/mineral supplement will help fill in the missing gaps. Be careful not to use travelling as an excuse to be slack with your diet.
Low energy (kilojoule/calorie) intake: For athletes such as gymnasts, figure skaters and dancers who need to keep slim or for those who are dieting to lose weight, a multi-vitamin/mineral supplement is an added assurance that they obtain the full range of vitamins and minerals on a daily basis.
Iron deficiency (diagnosed by a blood test): Supplements of iron, perhaps in conjunction with Vitamin C, will be useful (see page 43).
Inadequate calcium intake: Calcium supplements may be necessary for a person who fails to meet their daily calcium requirements. They should of course make their very best effort with calcium-rich foods.

PLACEBO EFFECT

A placebo is a substance which performs no physiological function but which may benefit the taker psychologically. In other words, if you think or believe that something might help you then it's highly likely that it will.

Nutrition supplements can have a powerful psychological effect. This is one of the main reasons why so many supplements with no proven benefits remain popular. Unfortunately, many studies investigating the benefits of supplements have not taken the placebo effect into account. In these studies the true response due to the supplements is impossible to determine. A large proportion of studies investigating nutrition supplements have been poorly designed, making any conclusions from them meaningless.

Testimonials made by athletes are bound to contain an element of the placebo effect. Often these testimonials are the only support the supplement has to stand on. Clearly, there is a need for well-designed, scientific research in this area which would provide us with information about supplements that we can use with greater confidence.

INDEX

Tuna and Corn 15

Oaty Orange Biscuits 68
Orange Oaty Biscuits 68

Paella 48
Pancakes 70
Pasta
  see also Lasagne
  with Cheese Sauce 40
  Honey Soy Noodles 14
  with Marinara Sauce 40
  with Mushroom and Ham
    Sauce 40
  and Spinach Salad 22
  with Tomato, Chilli and
    Herb Sauce 40
  Tuna and Corn Noodles 15
Peach and Apricot
  Smoothie 33
Pear and Yogurt Porridge 9
Pie
  Ham and Egg 9
  Rice 48
Pikelets 16
Pineapple
  and Apricot Muffins 13
  Crush 33
Pitta
  Crisps 14
  Pizzas 54
Pizzas
  Chicken 54
  Herb and Onion 52
  Pitta 54
Plum Sauce 56
Pork
  Fruity 44
  with Plum Sauce 56
Porridge 9
Potato Salad 27
Powershake 33
Prawns and Chicken Paella 48
Pumpkin
  Muffins 13
  Fruit Cake 68
Quiche, Salmon Bread 24

Rice
  Banana Custard 16
  Chicken and Parmesan
    Risotto 48
  Fried 48
  Pie 48
  Spiced 48
Roast 42
Rockmelon Crush 33

Salad
  Bread Pockets 26
  Chicken, with Herb
    Mayonnaise 22
  Citrus and Nectarine 22
  Potato 27
  Spinach and Pasta 22
  Tuna, with Curry
    Mayonnaise 26
Salmon Bread Quiche 24
Sandwiches
  Fillings 25
  Steak 58
Satay Sauce 26
Sauce
  Ginger Chilli 56
  Plum 56
  Satay 26
  Tartare 58
Scones, Cheese and Chive 13
Sesame Beef 56
Smoothies 33
Soya Burgers 58
Spiced Rice 48
Spinach and Pasta Salad 22
Sponge, Strawberry 70
Steak Sandwiches 58
Steamed Jam Pudding 73
Stir-Fry
  Chilli Chicken 44
  Curry Lamb 45
  Vegetable 44
Strawberry
  Dip 66
  Milkshake 33
  Sponge 70
Sweet and Sour Chicken 52

Tandoori
  Chicken 38
  Lamb 38
Tartare Sauce 58
Thai Beef 44
Tomato Chilli and Herb Pasta
  Sauce 40
Tuna
  and Corn Noodles 15
  Lasagne 72
  Salad with Curry
    Mayonnaise 26
Turkey Bakes 24

Vanilla Milkshake 33
Vegetables
  Lasagne 46
  Roast 42
  Stir-Fry 44

Watermelon Crush 33

Orton Gillingham Tools For Kids With Dyslexia

100 activities to help children with dyslexia differentiate and correctly use "b", "d", "p" and "q" letters

BRAINCHILD

This workbook belongs to:

_____

_____

_____

Introduction

Teaching a child with dyslexia to read:

Dyslexia is a specific and persistent learning disability that affects reading and writing. For children with dyslexia, learning to read and write can be a difficult challenge for families and educators to tackle. For these children, written language becomes a great barrier, often without meaning or logic, which generates rejection of the task, frustration and discomfort.

The child with dyslexia is a child who has significant difficulties in reading and writing, because their brain processes information differently than other children; which is why if we expect the same results following the traditional method, we will find many barriers that can and often do harm the child. It is important to become aware of the characteristics of this difficulty, so as to help the child learn to read and the consequent overcoming of their difficulties such as understanding, knowledge and attention to their needs.

Reading difficulties with dyslexia

Dyslexia is a learning disability of neurobiological origin, which causes seem to be in the maturation and structuring of certain brain structures.

Dyslexia is therefore a condition of the brain which causes it to process information differently, making it difficult for the person to understand letters, their sounds, their combinations, etc.

Human language is a language based on signs, letters and their sounds, which are arbitrary. The correspondence of each grapheme (letter) with its phoneme (sound), does not follow any logic; it's simply chance. This is one of the greatest difficulties that children face when they have to learn to read and write. Converting the spoken language, they know into signs and transforming sounds into letters is a challenge.

This is even more complicated in children with dyslexia; the relationship becomes something indecipherable for them. No matter how hard they try, they cannot make sense of that dance between letters and sounds.

Children with dyslexia have a lot of difficulty recognizing letters, sometimes they mistake letters for others, write them backwards, etc.

Another difficulty they face, is knowing the sound that corresponds to each letter, and things get even more complicated when we combine several letters and we have to know several sounds.

New words are a challenge for them and they can forget them easily, so they must work hard to acquire them.

Sometimes they read certain words effortlessly, but the next day they completely forget them.

When they write, they omit letters, change their position, forget words in a sentence, etc.

Dyslexia also affects reading comprehension. When they read, they are trying really hard to decipher and understand each word, sometimes even each letter; that is why the meaning of the text gets lost.

Reading comprehension: Activities to help develop it in children.

How to teach a child with dyslexia to read

A child with dyslexia has difficulty learning to read and write, because it is hard for them to recognize letters and know which sound they correspond to. However, the child can learn to read and write and overcome those difficulties. Remember that dyslexia is a learning difficulty that does not imply any physical or mental handicap; the child with dyslexia has adequate capacities. In order to teach a child with dyslexia to read, it is essential to know the nature of their difficulties, understand them and use a teaching method that responds to their needs.

A child with dyslexia

A teaching method to help a child with dyslexia read

In the first place, it is necessary to make an assessment of the child, to know their reading and writing level, the nature and characteristics of their difficulties in order to understand their specific needs. For this, it is advisable to seek a specialist.

Reading favors the development of phonological awareness (which consists of the correspondence of the sound with the letter). To do this, start with simple activities, letter by letter. Even if other children around the same age read full texts, it may be necessary to start working letter by letter. Later, we can continue with the words, phrases and texts. It is about dedicating more time and more detail to the learning process.

Phonological awareness worksheets

Use motivational activities that are engaging. Do not limit the child to just paper and pencil: they can make letters out of play dough, write on sand with their fingers, play catch or games such as hangman, word searches, crossword puzzles, etc.

Don't force them to read or read a lot. Try to have them read on a daily basis, little by little; sometimes a sentence or a paragraph is enough. Help them understand what they read, ask them questions, ask them to read again, etc.

Read & Trace "b"

Read and trace the b's. Say the name of each picture. Color them.

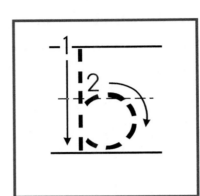

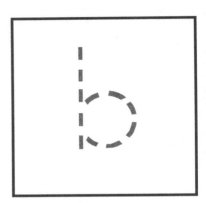

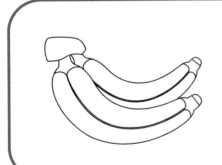

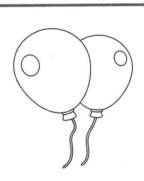

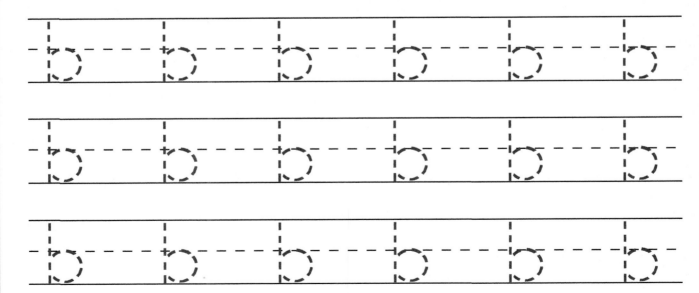

Read & Trace "d"

Read and trace the d's. Say the name of each picture. Color them.

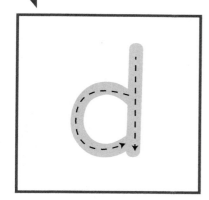
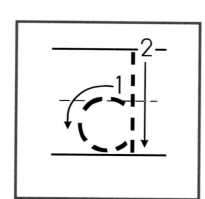
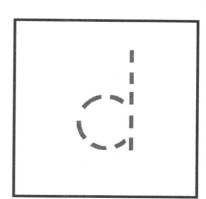

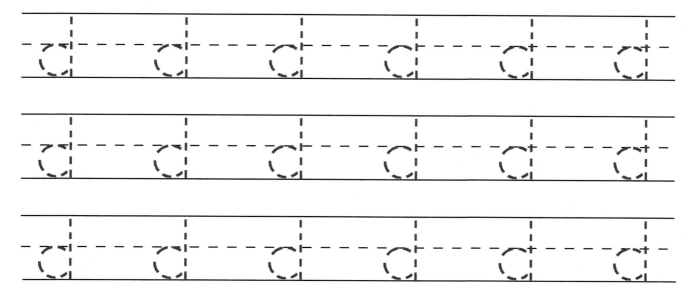

Read & Trace "p"

Read and trace the p's. Say the name of each picture. Color them.

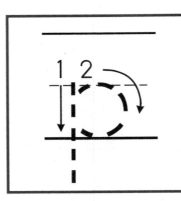

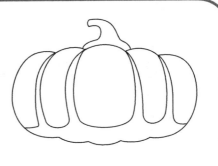

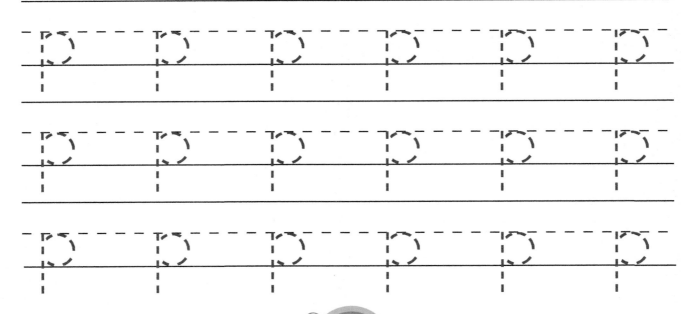

Read & Trace "q"

Read and trace the q's. Say the name of each picture. Color them.

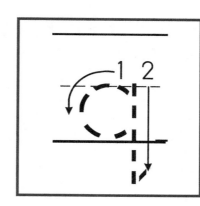

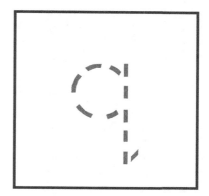

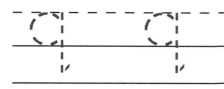
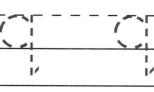
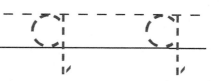

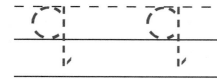
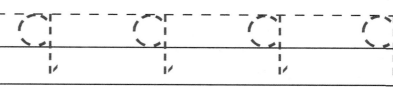

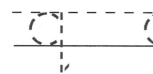
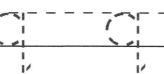
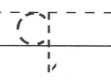
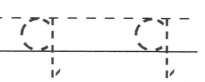

Say & Write "b"

Say and trace the b's. Write the letter in each box.

Say: Start at the top go down up around!

 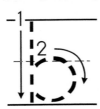 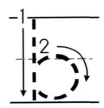 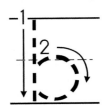

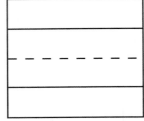 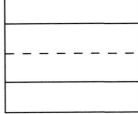 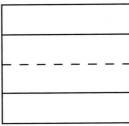

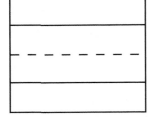 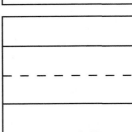 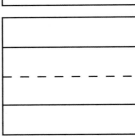

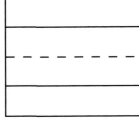 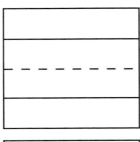 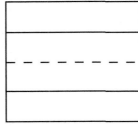

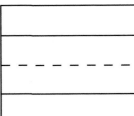 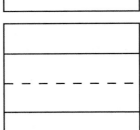 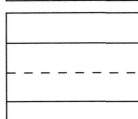

9

Say & Write "d"

Say and trace the d's. Write the letter in each box.

Say: Push around up down!

Say & Write "p"

Say and trace the p's. Write the letter in each box.

Say: Start in the middle go down up around!

Say & Write "q"

Say and trace the q's. Write the letter in each box.

Say: Push around down flag!

Trace with Finger

Say and trace the b's with your finger using poster paint. One is done for you.

Say: Start at the top go down up around!

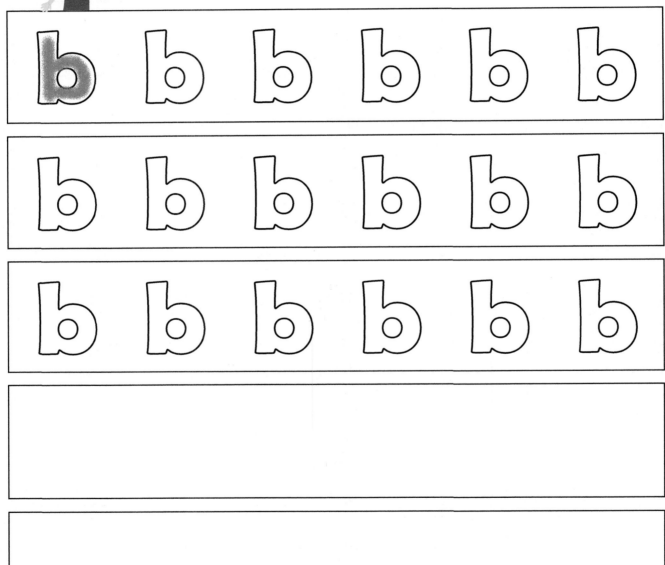

b b b b b b

b b b b b b

b b b b b b

Trace with Finger

Say and trace the d's with your finger using poster paint. One is done for you.

Say: Push around up down!

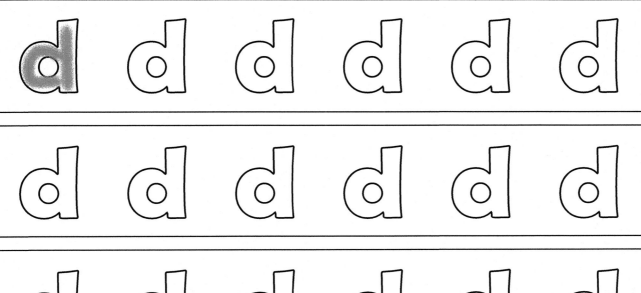

Trace with Finger

Say and trace the p's with your finger using poster paint. One is done for you.

Say: Start in the middle go down up around!

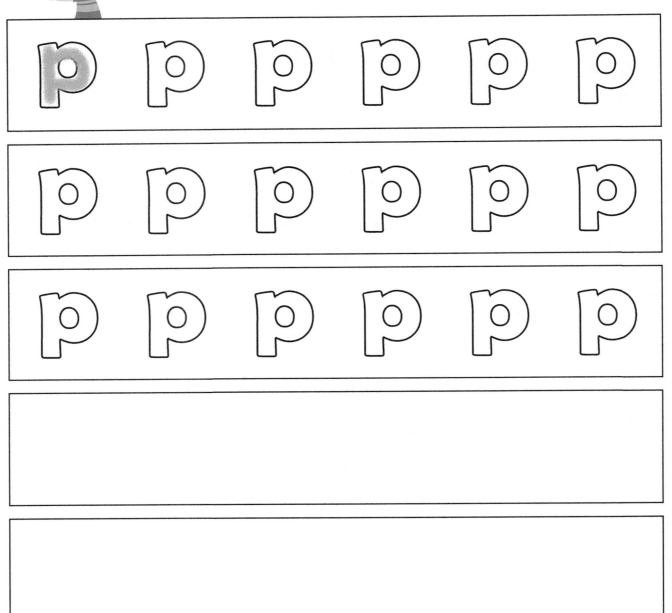

Trace with Finger

Say and trace the q's with your finger using poster paint. One is done for you.

Say: Push around down flag!

Write & Color "b"

Write the b's in the blanks. Color them with green color.

b   b

b   b

b   b

b   b

b   b

Find & Circle

b   b   q   b   b   p

p   d   b   d   b

b   b   b   b   q   b

q   p   b   d   b

d   b   b   d   p   b

b   d   b   b   p

b   b   b   q   d   b

q   d   b   b   b

b   d   b   d   p   b

18

Write & Color "d"

Write the d's in the blanks. Color them with pink color.

------- d ------- d

------- d ------- d

------- d ------- d

------- d ------- d

------- d ------- d

Find & Circle

b   d   q   b   d   p

d   d   d   d   b

b   d   b   d   d   b

q   d   b   d   d

d   d   b   d   p   d

b   d   b   d   p

b   d   b   d   d   b

q   d   d   b   d

b   d   b   d   d   b

20

Write & Color "p"

Write the p's in the blanks. Color them with blue color.

p

p

p

p

p

p

p

p

p

p

Find & Circle

p   d   p   b   p   p

p   d   d   p   b

b   p   b   p   d   p

q   p   p   p   d

d   p   q   d   p   d

b   p   q   p   p

b   d   q   d   q   q

q   p   d   b   p

b   p   b   p   d   q

Write & Color "q"

Write the q's in the blanks. Color them with orange color.

q

q

q

q

q

q

q

q

q

q

Find & Circle

q   d   q   b   p   q

p   d   q   p   q

b   q   q   p   q   p

q   q   p   q   d

q   p   q   d   q   p

b   q   q   p   p

b   q   q   q   q

q   p   d   q   q

b   q   b   p   d   q

Stamp & Write "b"

Say "down up around." Write the b and then stamp a b.

b

25

Find & Color

 b

 d

 b

 b

 p

 d

 q

 b

 d

 b

 b

 p

 b

 q

 b

 b

 p

 d

 b

 q

 b

 b

 p

 d

 b

Stamp & Write "d"

Say "push around up down." Write the d and then stamp a d.

d

Find & Color

d

d	b	q	p
p	d	b	d
d	b	d	p
p	d	b	d
d	d	q	b
d	p	b	d
p	d	q	d

Stamp & Write "p"

Say "down up around." Write the p and then stamp a p.

p

29

Find & Color

p	q	b	d	p
q	p	q	p	q
p	d	p	q	p
p	q	b	p	q
p	q	p	d	q

Stamp & Write "q"

Say "push around down flag." Write the q and then stamp a q.

q

Find & Color

q

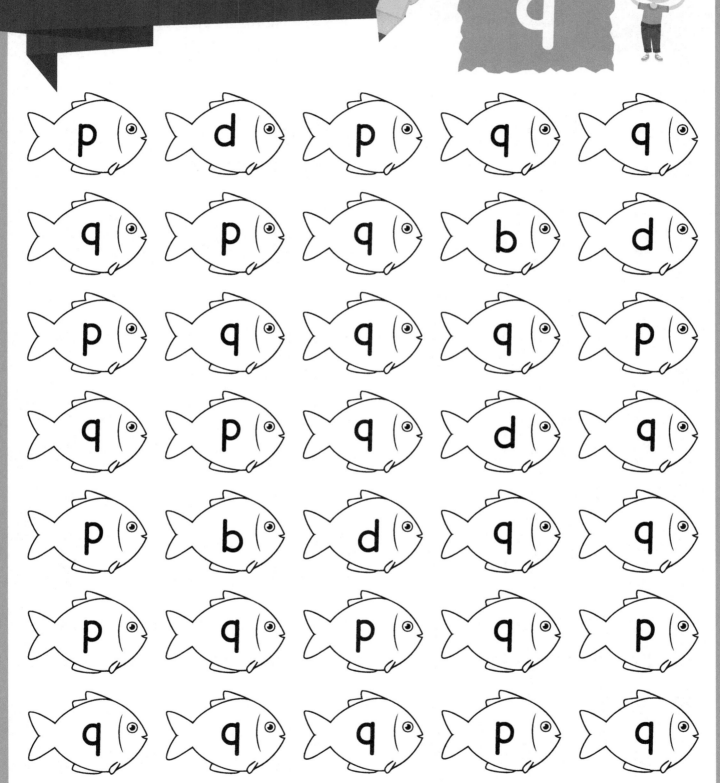

Track & Loop "b"

Start from the bee make a line under each letter. Only loop the letter b. One has been done for you.

d b b d b b d d b

b b b d b d b d b

d d b b d b b d d

b d b d b d b d b

b d d b b b d b d

b d b b d b d b d

d d b b b b d b b

33

What's My Sound?

Look at the pictures. Shade the beginning sound of each picture.

q	p

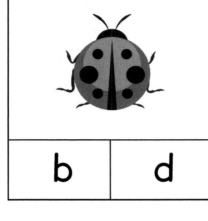

b	d

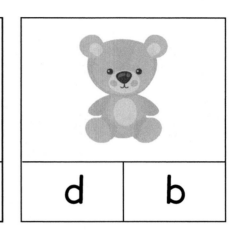

d	b

p	d

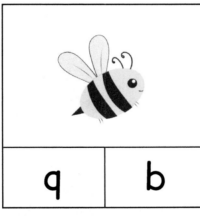

q	b

q	p

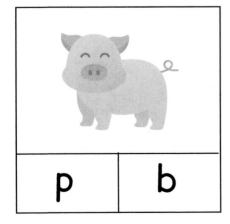

p	b

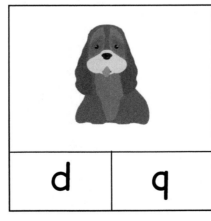

d	q

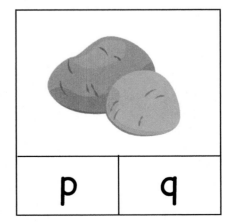

p	q

Track & Loop "d"

Start from the duck make a line under each letter. Only loop the letter d. One has been done for you.

d d b d d b d b d

d b d d d b d d b

b d d b b d d b d

d b d b d b d b d

b d d b d b d b d

d b b d d b d d b

d d b b b d b d b

Circle the Sound

Look at the pictures. Circle the beginning sound of each picture.

	b / d		p / q
	q / p		d / b
	p / q		d / b
	b / d		d / b

36

Track & Loop "p"

Start from the pig make a line under each letter. Only loop the letter p. One has been done for you.

p q p q p q q p p

q q p p q p q p q

q p p q p p q p q

p q q p p q q p q

q q p p q q p q p q

p p p q p q p q p

q p p q q q p q p

Missing Sounds

Fill in the missing sound of each picture. Write the word in the sentence.

	___ ack	There is a bug on her _____.
	___ ress	I love that _____.
	___ ag	Where is my _____.
	___ ot	Fill the _____ with water.
	___ ueen	She is a _____.

Track & Loop "q"

Start from the quail make a line under each letter. Only loop the letter q. One has been done for you.

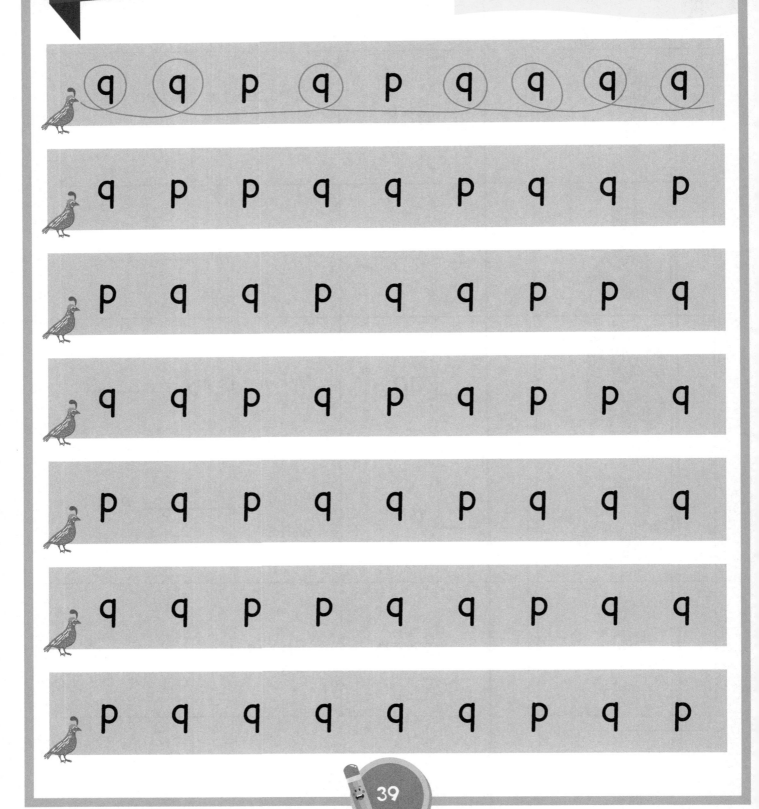

q q p q p q q q q

q p p q q p q q p

p q q p q q p p q

q q p q p q p p q

p q p q q p q q q

q q p p q q p q q

p q q q q q q p q

Circle & Write

Look at the pictures.
Circle the correct spelling.
Write the word.

dig did	pant dant	dow bow
___ _ _ _ _ ___	___ _ _ _ _ ___	___ _ _ _ _ ___
dop box	ball bell	pot pop
___ _ _ _ _ ___	___ _ _ _ _ ___	___ _ _ _ _ ___
bird quail	pan pen	dip dig
___ _ _ _ _ ___	___ _ _ _ _ ___	___ _ _ _ _ ___

Track & Loop "b,d"

Start from the dot make a line under each letter. Only loop the letters b,d. One has been done for you.

• b q d b p d q b d

• b d p d q b p q d

• p d b p b q d b q

• d p q b d q d p b

• b p d b q d p b d

• d p d b p b d b d

• p d b q p b d q b

Missing Sounds

Fill in the missing sound of each picture. Write the word in the sentence.

	__ ath	He is taking a _____.
	__ ish	Put some food in the _____.
	__ ig	He can _____ the soft sand.
	__ ell	He rang the _____.
	__ oll	I have a _____.

Track & Loop "p,q"

Start from the dot make a line under each letter. Only loop the letters p,q. One has been done for you.

• p   q   d   b   p   q   q   d   p

• p   d   q   b   p   q   d   q   d

• d   p   q   p   q   b   p   q   b

• q   q   p   b   q   d   p   q   p

• p   q   d   b   p   q   d   p   q

• q   d   p   b   q   d   p   q   d

• p   p   b   q   p   q   d   q   p

43

Find & Color

Look at the pictures. Find and color the correct beginning sound.

b	p	q	d

q	p	d	b

p	q	d	b

p	d	q	b

b	q	p	d

Roll & Write

Roll a die and write a letter. Say the letter as you write it.

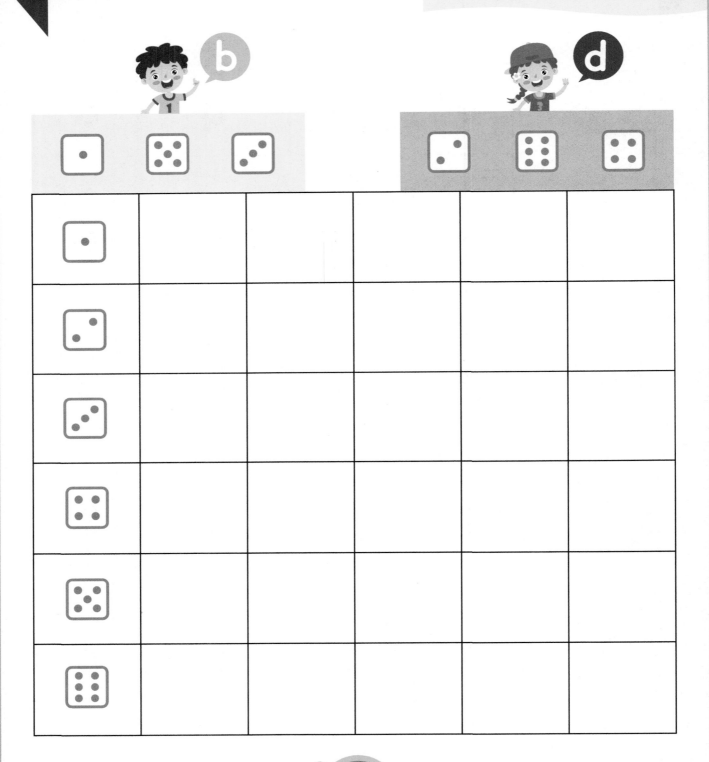

Color by Code

Use the code to color the balloon.

b=Red   d=Green

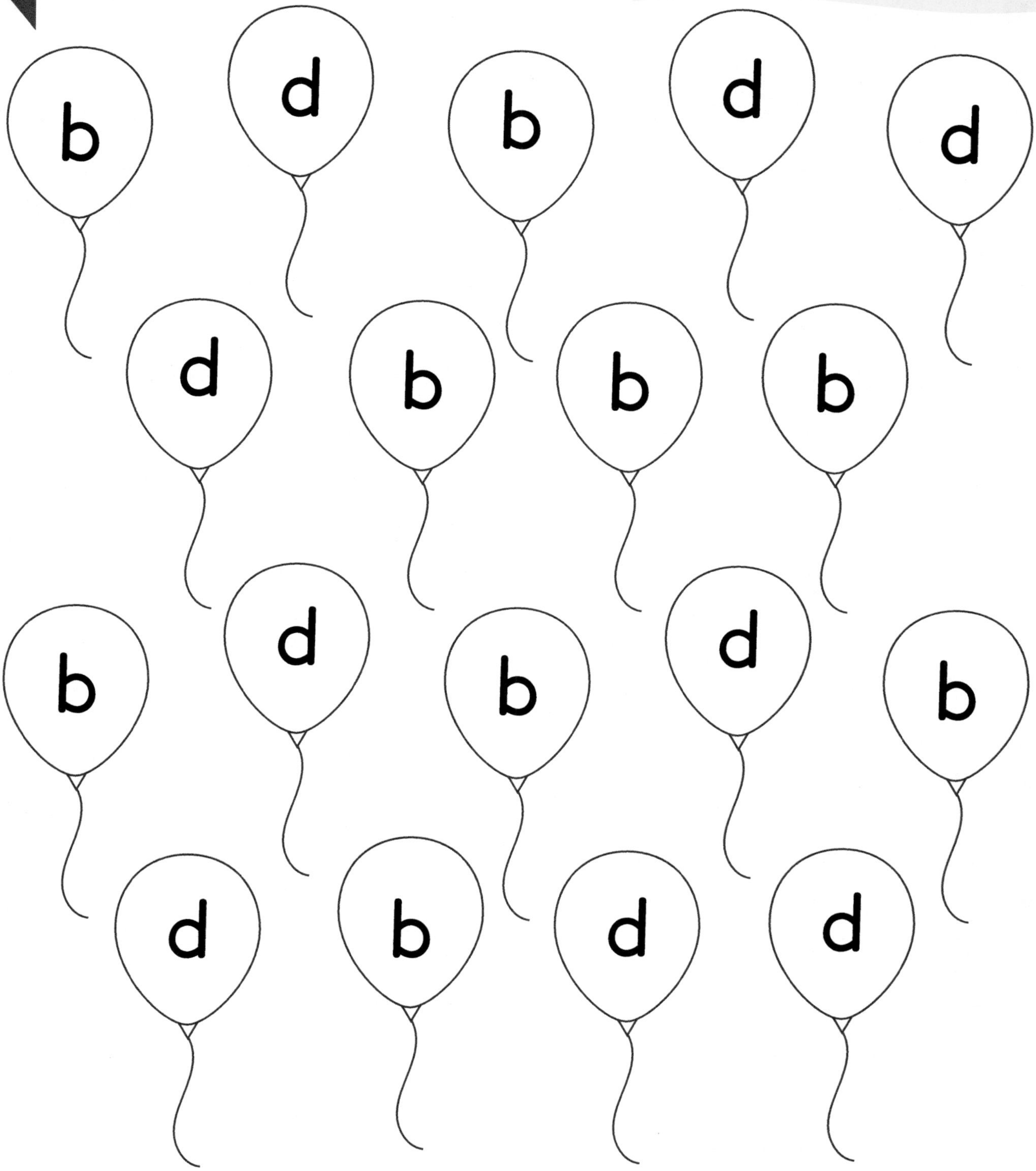

b d b d d

d b b b

b d b d b

d b d d

Roll & Write

Roll a die and write a letter. Say the letter as you write it.

P

q

[die 1]					
[die 1]					
[die 2]					
[die 3]					
[die 4]					
[die 5]					
[die 6]					

Color by Code

Use the code to color the pear.

p=Yellow   q=Pink

Roll & Write

Roll a die and write a letter. Say the letter as you write it.

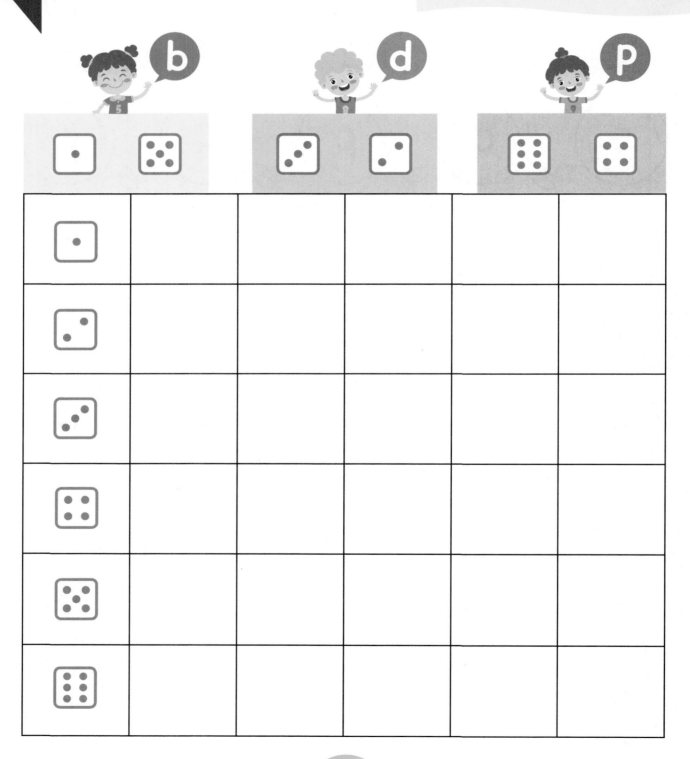

Color by Code

Use the code to color the fish.

b=Red   d=Blue   p=Orange

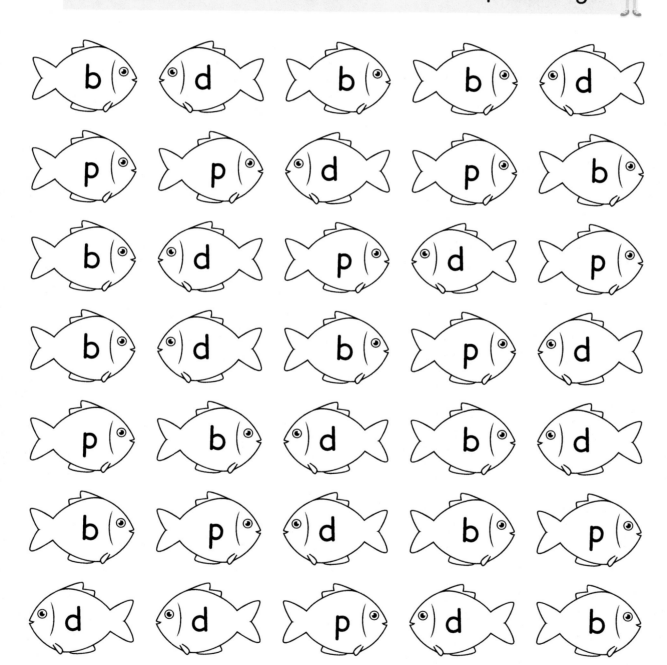

Roll & Write

Roll a die and write a letter. Say the letter as you write it.

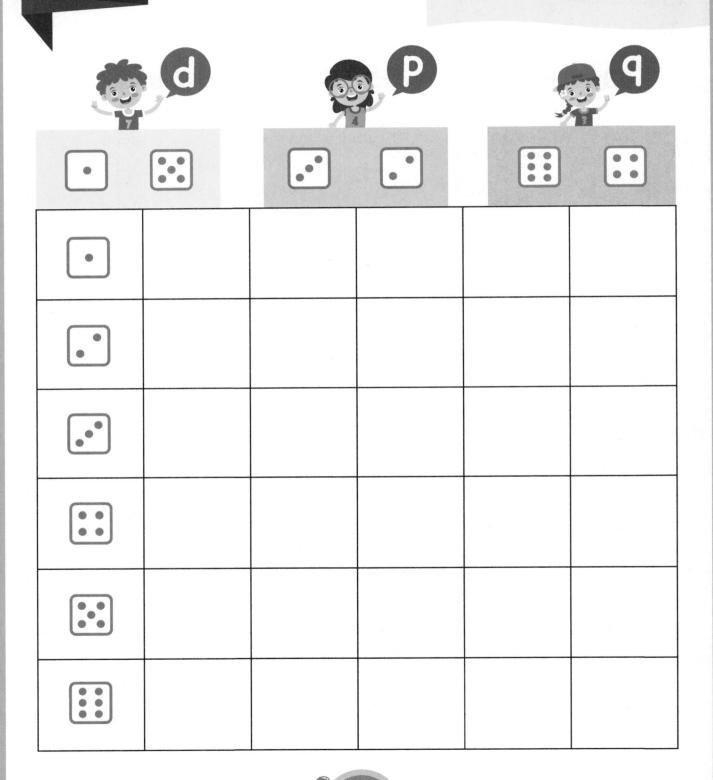

Color by Code

Use the code to color the kettle.

p=Purple   d=Green   q=Black

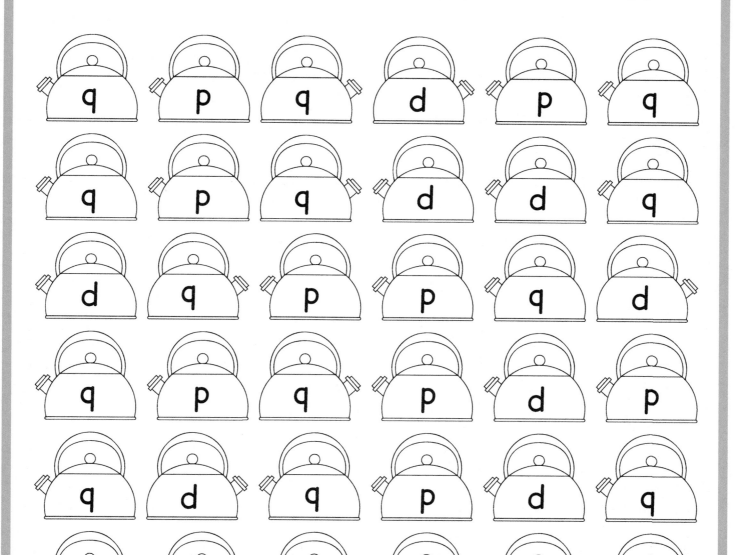

Roll & Write

Roll a die and write a letter. Say the letter as you write it.

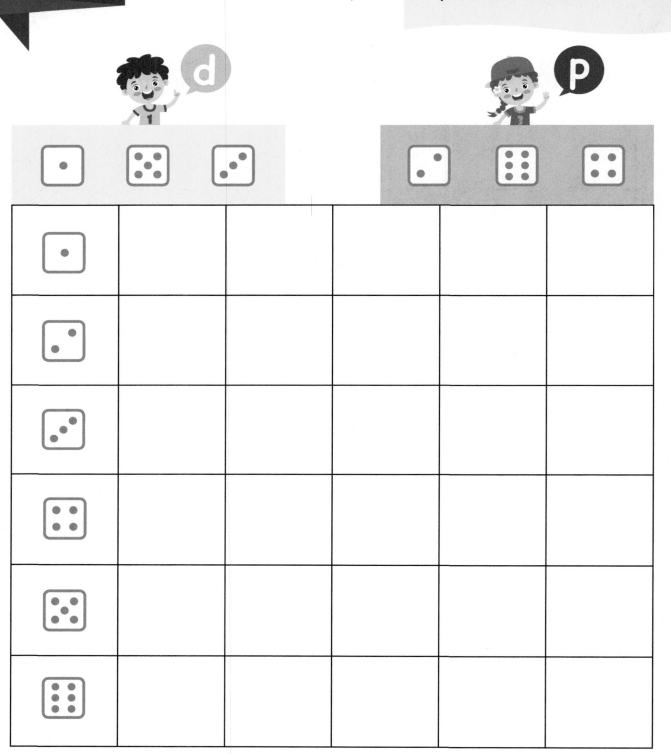

'b' & 'd' Words

Read the words. Color the 'b' words blue and 'd' words red.

bed	dad	bot	dot	bag	dew
dig	bat	dug	beg	bon	bad
bin	dag	bug	did	bun	day
dam	ban	bed	daw	din	bar
bid	dip	big	dill	bit	dan
dog	bum	dew	bud	dud	bus

Letter "b" Maze

Follow the letter b through the maze. Color them.

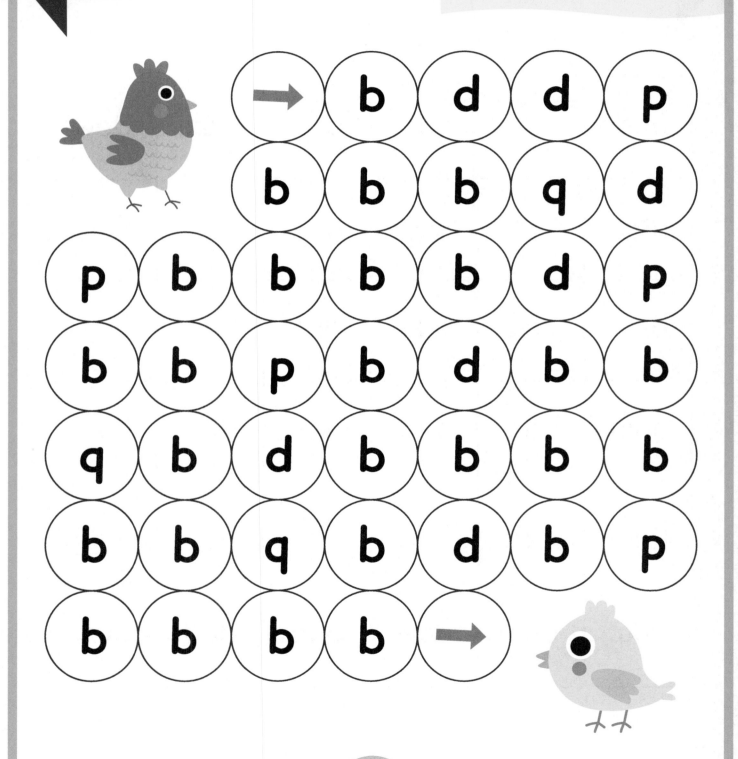

→ b d d p
b b b q d
p b b b b d p
b b p b d b b
q b d b b b b
b b q b d b p
b b b b →

55

'p' & 'q' Words

Read the words. Color the 'p' words red and 'q' words orange.

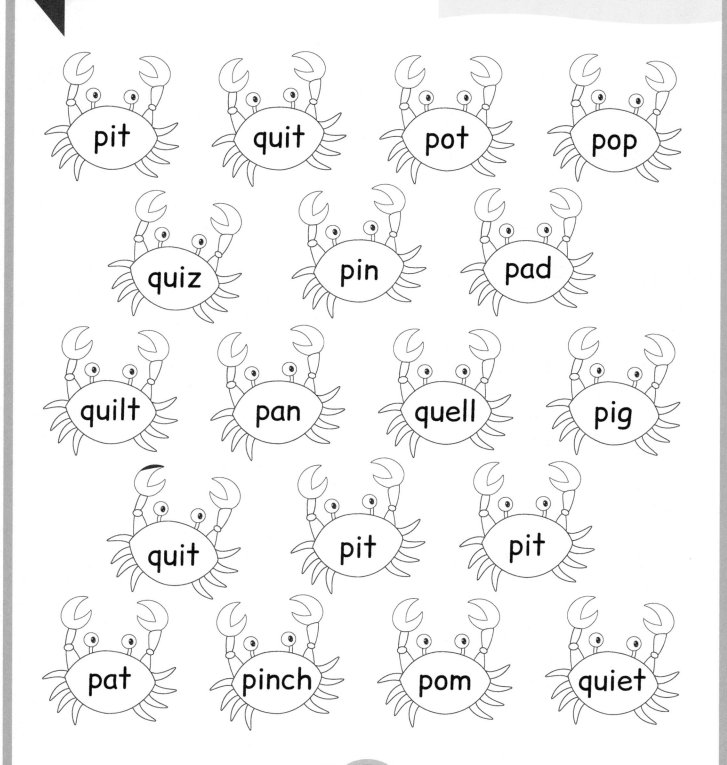

pit

quit

pot

pop

quiz

pin

pad

quilt

pan

quell

pig

quit

pit

pit

pat

pinch

pom

quiet

Letter "d" Maze

Follow the letter d through the maze. Color them.

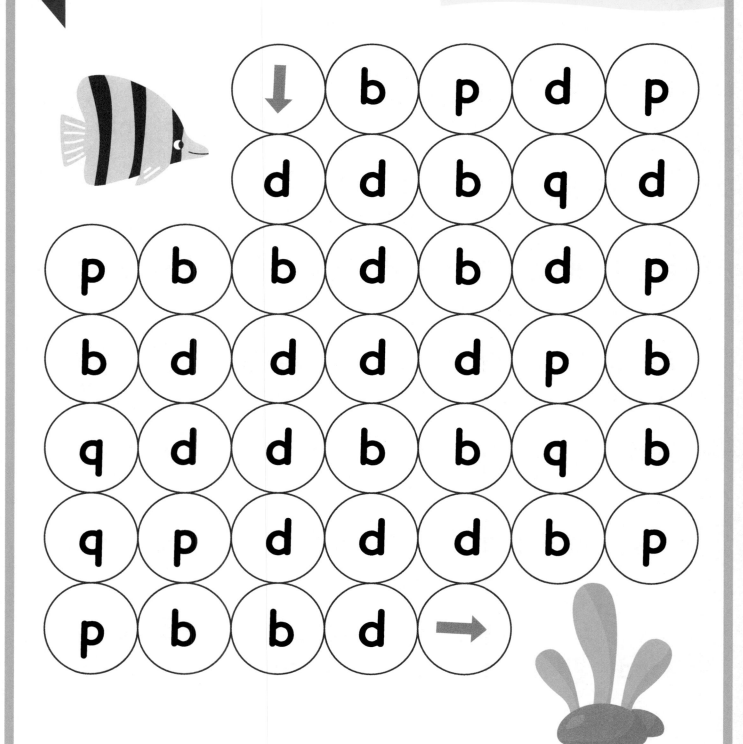

↓	b	p	d	p
d	d	b	q	d
p	b	b	d	b	d	p
b	d	d	d	d	p	b
q	d	d	b	b	q	b
q	p	d	d	d	b	p
p	b	b	d	→		

Read & Color

Read the words. Color the 'b' words yellow, 'd' words orange and 'p' words red.

back bop part drill dim

past ball pot dish blow

beg pink dark bug pinch

did pill but pad dog

den bet dig bun pit

Letter "p" Maze

Follow the letter p through the maze. Color them.

	↓	p	p	d	p
	d	d	p	q	d
p	b	b	d	p	p	p
b	d	d	d	d	p	b
q	d	p	p	p	p	b
q	p	p	d	d	b	p
d	p	p	p	→		

Color the Train

Read the words. Color the words using the code listed below.

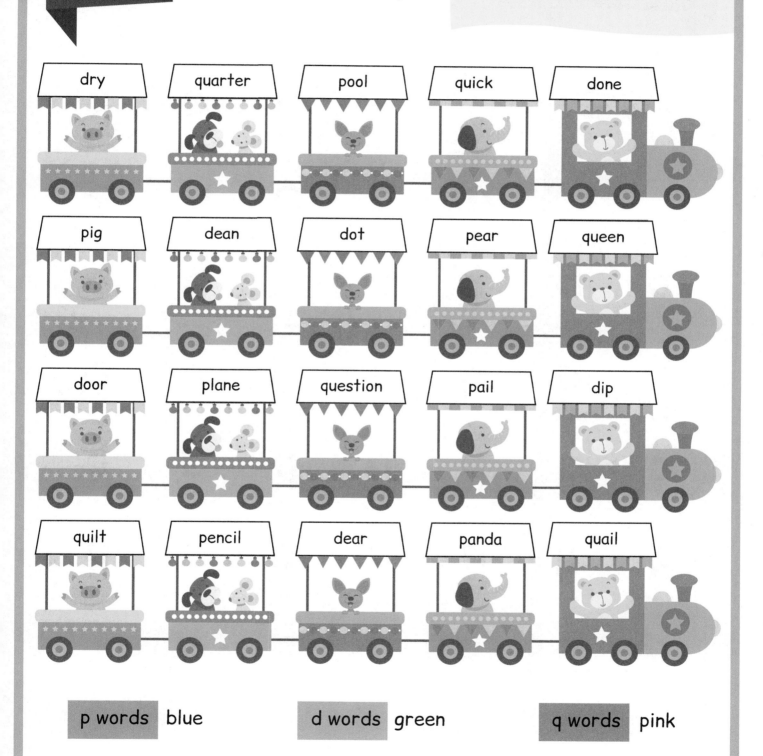

dry	quarter	pool	quick	done
pig	dean	dot	pear	queen
door	plane	question	pail	dip
quilt	pencil	dear	panda	quail

p words blue   d words green   q words pink

60

Letter "q" Maze

Follow the letter q through the maze. Color them.

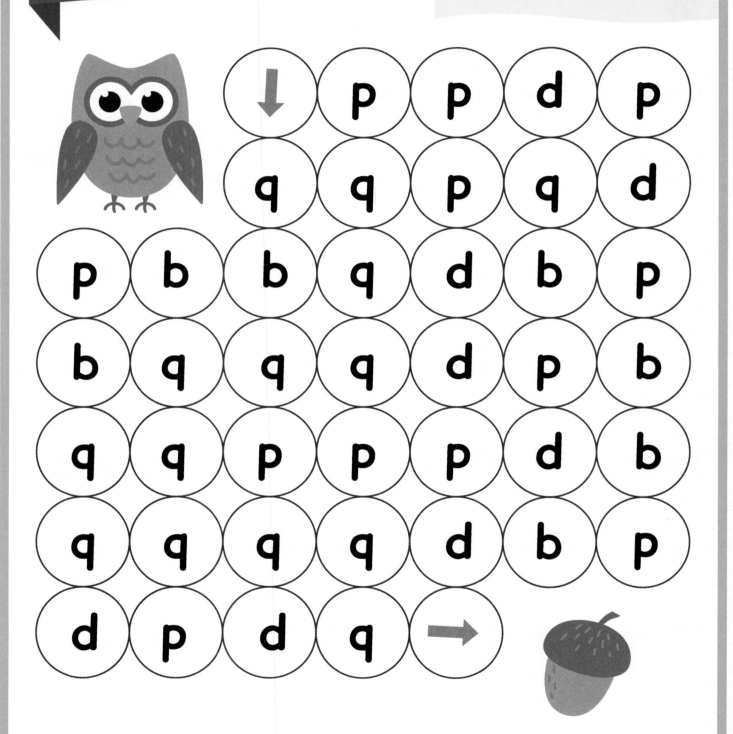

	↓	p	p	d	p
	q	q	p	q	d
p	b	b	q	d	b	p
b	q	q	q	d	p	b
q	q	p	p	p	d	b
q	q	q	q	d	b	p
d	p	d	q	→		

Color the Ice Cream

Read the words. Color the words using the code listed below.

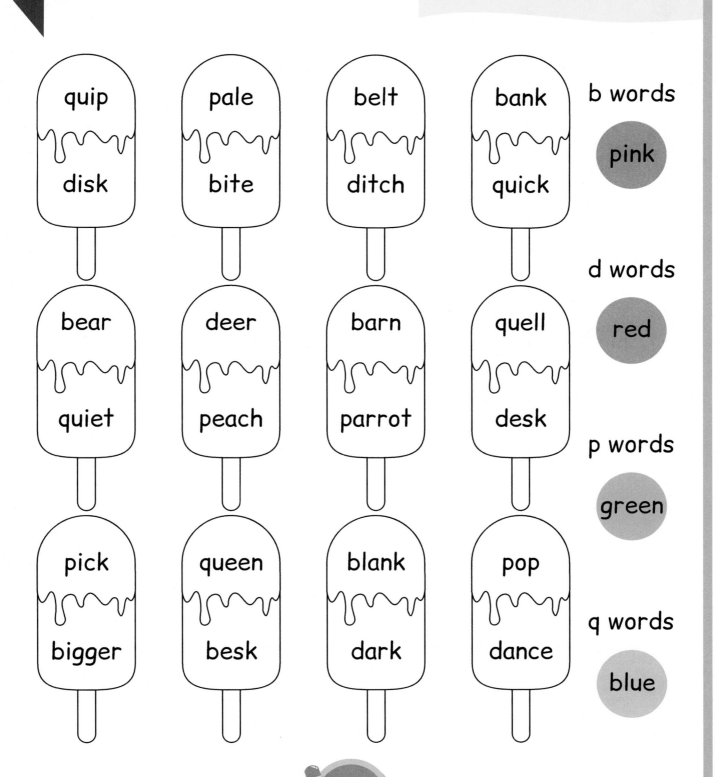

quip / disk	pale / bite	belt / ditch	bank / quick	**b words** — pink
bear / quiet	deer / peach	barn / parrot	quell / desk	**d words** — red
pick / bigger	queen / besk	blank / dark	pop / dance	**p words** — green
				q words — blue

Words Maze

Read the words. Help the bee find a way to the hive by coloring the boxes with 'b' and 'd' words.

bop	dirt	pot	quit	pink
pig	pan	big	bang	quell	pit
quick	pop	pen	dull	pan	pot
past	drag	dim	ban	palm	pet
quilt	book	door	page	pear	queen
page	dug	bat	bite	dad	

Read & Sort

Read the words. Sort the words into the correct boxes.

bed   dad   bat   big   dag

did   bag   dog   bun

dig   bin   dot   bus   dip

ball   den   box   dam

 'b' Words

 'd' Words

1. _____   2. _____

3. _____   4. _____

5. _____   6. _____

7. _____   8. _____

9. _____

1. _____   2. _____

3. _____   4. _____

5. _____   6. _____

7. _____   8. _____

9. _____

Words Maze

Read the words. Help the kid find a way to his home by coloring the boxes with 'p' and 'q' words.

bop	dirt	pot	bat	pink
quilt	push	palm	bang	big	pit
quick	pop	quid	pack	quill	pot
past	drag	dim	pain	bag	bear
dig	quit	quiz	page	done	bang
drum	quad	plant	pull	quick	

Read & Sort

Read the words. Sort the words into the correct boxes.

quick   pig   quilt   quell   Pan

pot   pit   quiz   page

quiet   quail   push   pop   quill

pick   quick   pom   quit

'p' Words

'q' Words

1. _____   2. _____

3. _____   4. _____

5. _____   6. _____

7. _____   8. _____

9. _____

1. _____   2. _____

3. _____   4. _____

5. _____   6. _____

7. _____   8. _____

9. _____

Count & Graph

Let's count the letters and color the graph.

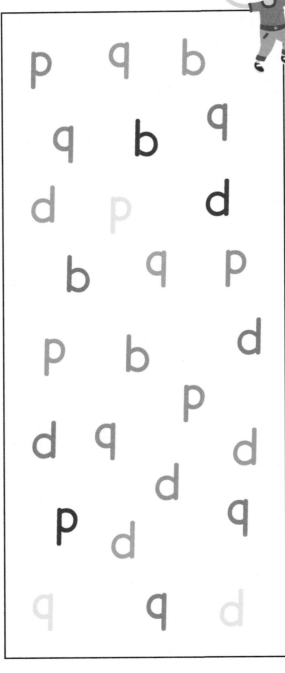

	b	d	p	q
10				
9				
8				
7				
6				
5				
4				
3				
2				
1				

Read & Sort

Read the words. Sort the words into the correct boxes.

park   date   boat   bear   duck

book   dish

pinch   deer

back

picnic

pick   bird   dance   party

'd' Words

1. _____

2. _____

3. _____

4. _____

5. _____

'p' Words

1. _____

2. _____

3. _____

4. _____

5. _____

'b' Words

1. _____

2. _____

3. _____

4. _____

5. _____

Graph the Words

Let's read the words. Graph the words by writing each in the correct column.

bot   dug   pot   Pat

pig   bit   quilt   dam   bad

dog   pan   bin   pin

5				
4				
3				
2				
1				
	b words	**d words**	**p words**	**q words**

Read & Highlight

Read the words and highlight them by using the code listed below.

p words purple

d words red

q words blue

dam

quick

pan

part

dirt

dig

quit

quail

done

pom

pack

dam

duck

dark

did

parrot

pot

queen

pig

date

dip

dug

pinch

Word Search

Find the hidden words listed below. Words can be up, down, or across.

n	a	b	l	y	j	b	x	s	n
u	q	f	r	h	b	a	c	k	q
q	u	e	e	n	p	p	j	x	u
x	i	d	u	m	p	x	c	d	i
i	l	n	i	j	e	a	c	u	t
c	l	y	k	b	p	i	n	c	h
b	e	n	d	o	p	j	c	k	o
d	p	o	o	l	x	a	f	r	n
d	c	s	h	d	k	h	e	p	x
r	b	x	q	d	e	s	z	k	b

back
bend
bold
dump
duck
pinch
pool
quit
quill
queen

71

Write the Words

Look at the pictures. Write the words in the blanks.

_____
- - - - - - - -
_____

_____
- - - - - - - -
_____

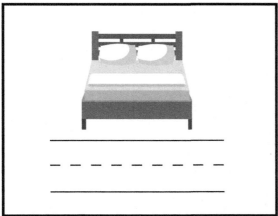

_____
- - - - - - - -
_____

_____
- - - - - - - -
_____

_____
- - - - - - - -
_____

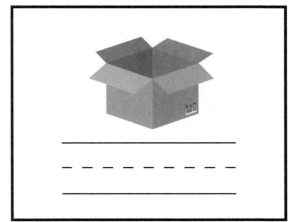

_____
- - - - - - - -
_____

Word Search

Find the hidden words listed below. Words can be up, down, or across.

d	v	z	j	b	e	s	t	n	r
r	m	y	p	i	n	c	h	q	i
i	e	q	t	g	y	y	u	e	u
n	o	u	m	g	n	p	s	d	l
k	v	i	h	e	p	c	q	f	i
h	i	l	x	r	e	w	m	n	x
s	n	t	d	b	a	o	q	t	d
w	p	a	o	o	r	j	f	z	u
u	s	t	o	b	b	o	o	h	i
g	p	a	r	k	q	d	a	m	d

bob
bigger
best
dam
drink
door
park
pinch
pear
quilt

Circle & Write

Look at the pictures.
Circle the correct spelling.
Write the word.

quilt quill	dig pig	bed bad
_____	_____	_____
bug bun	pray dry	bear bee
_____	_____	_____
bag bus	door poor	plane plain
_____	_____	_____

Word Search

Find the hidden words listed below. Words can be up, down, or across.

```
y  a  d  d  j  a  n  p  n  n
z  q  e  f  n  d  b  a  b  y
j  o  n  b  w  a  o  r  y  d
l  p  t  e  p  r  e  t  t  y
d  v  y  l  w  k  l  y  p  m
a  b  x  t  u  b  r  a  a  q
m  q  f  r  l  b  z  x  l  e
p  r  b  o  o  t  z  i  e  b
f  d  d  i  s  k  i  k  l  s
b  b  c  y  q  v  v  y  j  v
```

boot
belt
baby
dent
damp
disk
dark
pretty
party
pale

Missing Sounds

Fill in the missing sound of each picture. Write the word in the sentence.

	__ ig	Can you ride a _____.
	__ in	She has lost her _____.
	__ esk	He sat on the _____.
	__ uilt	He pulled off the _____.
	__ oor	Open the _____.

Word Search

Find the hidden words listed below. Words can be up, down, or across.

```
e  t  c  z  q  s  a  q  e  y
b  l  i  f  u  e  g  u  k  w
o  t  a  i  u  a  q  i  p  x
n  c  c  o  c  d  u  z  a  t
d  h  d  e  e  d  e  n  t  d
r  b  z  m  x  e  n  b  a  j
l  o  p  i  e  c  c  e  t  t
g  w  v  k  h  k  h  n  y  e
d  l  p  u  t  k  p  t  t  c
f  j  r  q  h  r  l  m  q  a
```

bent
bond
bowl
deck
deed
dent
pat
put
quiz
quench

Missing Sounds

Fill in the missing sound of each picture. Write the word in the sentence.

	__ izza	Do you like to eat _____.
	__ uick	He ran _____.
	__ uck	She has a black _____.
	__ ool	Kids are playing in the _____.
	__ rinks	He _____ cold water.

Scramble Words

Unscramble the words and write the correct word in the box. Use the words to make sentences.

Scramble Words	Unscramble Words	Sentences
a d d		
a t b		
o t p		
e b d		
o d g		

pot   bat   dog   dad   bed

Missing Sounds

Fill in the missing sound of each picture. Write the word in the sentence.

	__ icnic	We had a _____ last Sunday.
	__ un	I had a cup of tea and a _____.
	__ eer	Is it a _____?
	__ octor	He is a _____.
	__ uiet	Keep _____!

Scramble Words

Unscramble the words and write the correct word in the box. Use the words to make sentences.

Scramble Words	Unscramble Words	Sentences
i g p		
l a b l		
n e p		
u i q z		
g i d		

dig   quiz   ball   pig   pen

Roll & Color

b	d	P

⚀	b	b	b	b	b
⚁	d	d	d	d	d
⚂	d	d	d	d	d
⚃	p	p	p	p	p
⚄	b	b	b	b	b
⚅	p	p	p	p	p

82

Missing Sounds

Fill in the missing sound of each picture. Write the word in the sentence.

	__ ad	I love my _____.
	__ ear	She has a cute _____.
	__ uiz	He won the _____.
	__ ark	I go to the _____ daily.
	__ rum	Tom plays the _____.

Roll & Color

Roll a die and color the box with a letter. Say the letter as you color it. Use different colors.

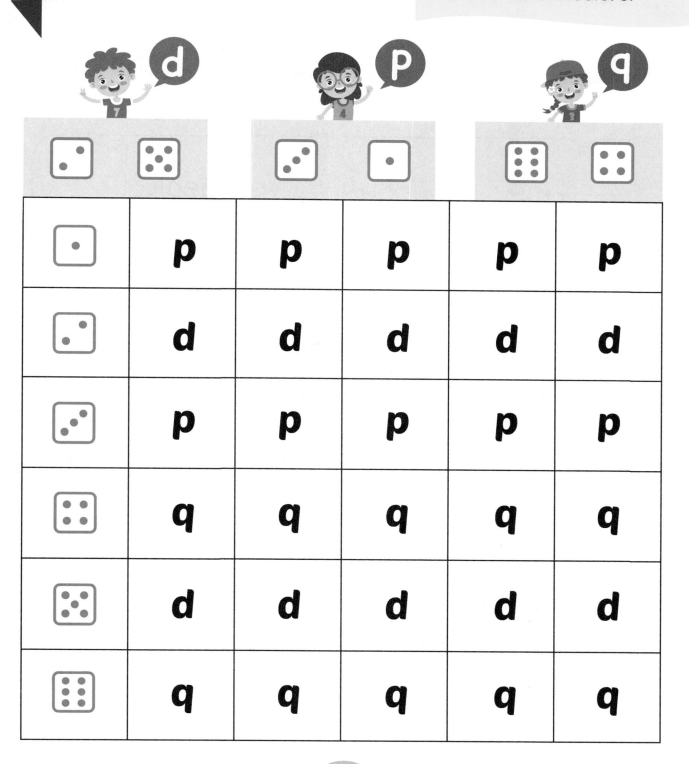

	p	p	p	p	p
	d	d	d	d	d
	p	p	p	p	p
	q	q	q	q	q
	d	d	d	d	d
	q	q	q	q	q

Read & Highlight

Read the words and highlight them by using the code listed below.

b words green   **p words** pink   **d words** orange

pearl   duty   peak

bush   dirt   dump

drop   done   purse   burst

drift   peer   drill   peace

blue

palace   perky

queen   bring

dress

blow   burn   pinch

Scramble Words

Unscramble the words and write the correct word in the box. Use the words to make sentences.

Scramble Words	Unscramble Words	Sentences
u b l e		
r t i d y		
y o b		
o w b		
p i d		

bow   blue   dip   boy   dirty

Make Sentences

Fill in the missing letter using the given letters. Use the words in your own sentences.

b	d	p	q

_____ arrot

1. _____
_____

_____ rink

2. _____
_____

_____ us

3. _____
_____

_____ ook

4. _____
_____

_____ ottle

5. _____
_____

Coloring by Words

Color the picture using the color codes listed below.

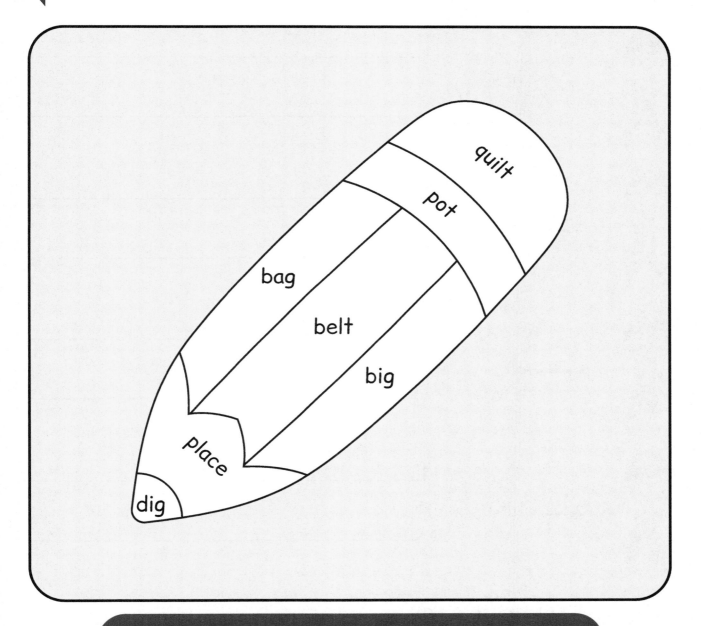

b words = blue	**d words = black**
p words = orange	**q words = pink**

Make Sentences

Fill in the missing letter using the given letters. Use the words in your own sentences.

b	d	p	q

_____ uck

1. ______________________________

____

_____ ress

2. ______________________________

____

_____ uy

3. ______________________________

____

_____ uiet

4. ______________________________

____

_____ arty

5. ______________________________

____

Coloring by Words

Color the picture using the color codes listed below.

b words = red	d words = orange
p words = pink	q words = yellow

Make the Sentences

Fill in the missing letter using the given letters. Use the words in your own sentences.

b	d	p	q

_____ raw

1._____

_____

_____ each

2._____

_____

_____ ubble

3._____

_____

_____ reak

4._____

_____

_____ oor

5._____

_____

91

Coloring by Words

Color the picture using the color codes listed below.

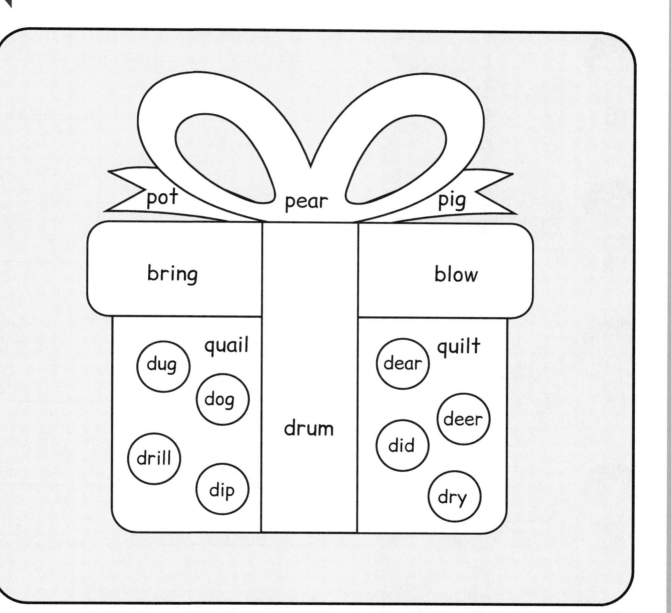

pot   pear   pig

bring   blow

quail   dug   dog   drill   dip

drum

quilt   dear   deer   did   dry

b words = pink   d words = yellow

p words =blue   q words = purple

Make the Sentences

Fill in the missing letter using the given letters. Use the words in your own sentences.

b d p q

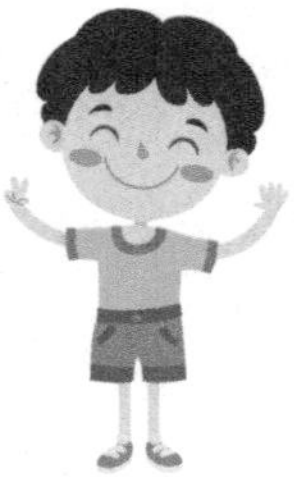

_____ oll

1. ______________________________

____

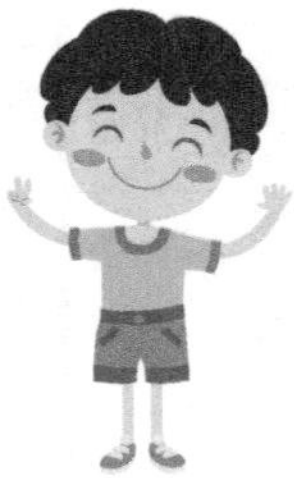

_____ ish

2. ______________________________

____

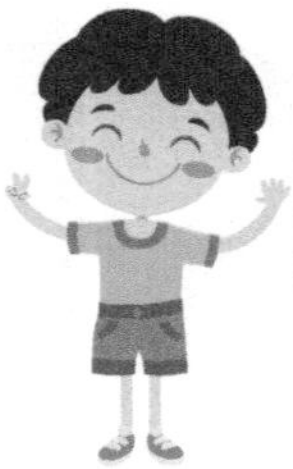

_____ oat

3. ______________________________

____

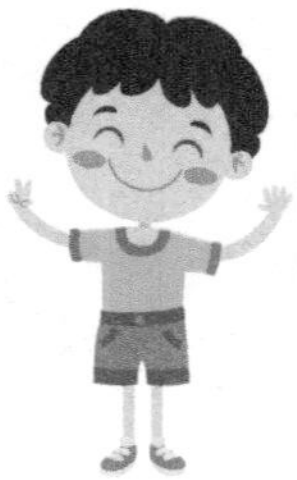

_____ ody

4. ______________________________

____

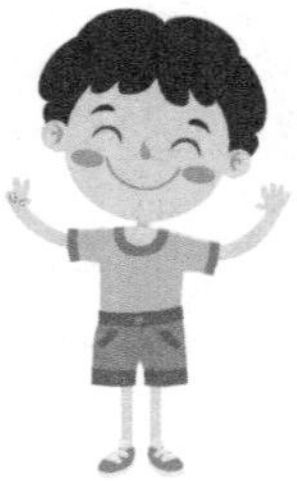

_____ alm

5. ______________________________

____

Coloring by Words

Color the picture using the color codes listed below.

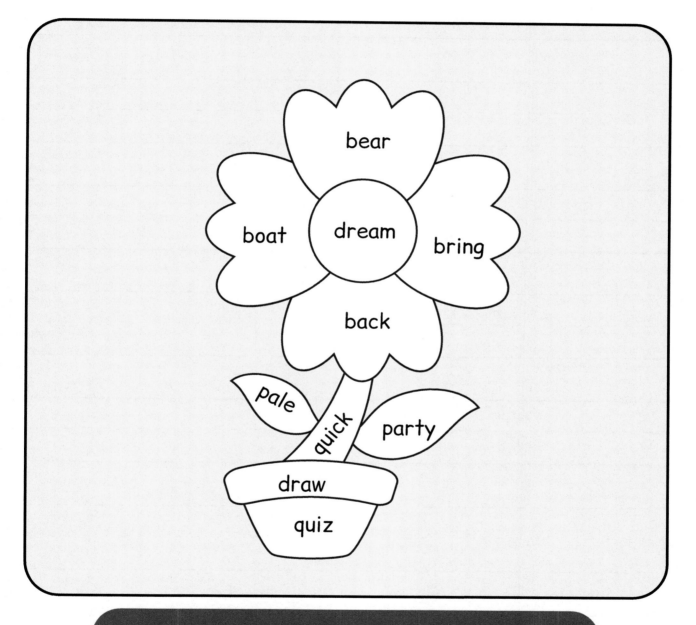

b words = blue   d words = yellow

p words = green   q words = brown

Practice Letter "b"

Practice Letter "d"

Practice Letter "p"

Practice Letter "q"

Practice "b" Words

1. _____

2. _____

3. _____

4. _____

5. _____

6. _____

7. _____

8. _____

9. _____

10. _____

11. _____

12. _____

13. _____

14. _____

Practice "d" Words

1. _____

2. _____

3. _____

4. _____

5. _____

6. _____

7. _____

8. _____

9. _____

10. _____

11. _____

12. _____

13. _____

14. _____

Practice "p" Words

1.

2.

3.

4.

5.

6.

7.

8.

9.

10.

11.

12.

13.

14.

Practice "q" Words

1. _____

2. _____

3. _____

4. _____

5. _____

6. _____

7. _____

8. _____

9. _____

10. _____

11. _____

12. _____

13. _____

14. _____

Reading Race

Read the columns as fast as you can.

did	dog	bed
bid	pod	ball
bit	pan	bag
dot	dan	pig
pot	dill	pom
dad	bet	pop
bad	dim	quill
pat	dam	bug

How fast can you read it? Mention the time.

	Mon	Tue	Wed	Thu	Fri
Time					

Reading Race

Read the columns as fast as you can.

deed	page	quit
bond	bring	quench
draw	peace	buzz
done	peak	pray
bear	dance	quiz
back	dent	queen
bone	damp	quilt
pear	quip	park

How fast can you read it? Mention the time.

	Mon	Tue	Wed	Thu	Fri
Time					

Printed in Great Britain
by Amazon

43211132R00059

Collins

INTERNATIONAL PRIMARY ENGLISH

Workbook 2

William Collins' dream of knowledge for all began with the publication of his first book in 1819. A self-educated mill worker, he not only enriched millions of lives, but also founded a flourishing publishing house. Today, staying true to this spirit, Collins books are packed with inspiration, innovation and practical expertise. They place you at the centre of a world of possibility and give you exactly what you need to explore it.

Collins. Freedom to teach.

An imprint of HarperCollins*Publishers*
The News Building
1 London Bridge Street
London SE1 9GF

browse the complete Collins catalogue at
www.collins.co.uk

10 9 8 7 6 5 4 3 2

ISBN 978-0-00-814764-8

British Library Cataloguing in Publication Data
A catalogue record for this publication is available from the British Library.

Publisher Celia Wigley
Publishing manager Karen Jamieson
Commissioning editor Lucy Cooper
Series editor Karen Morrison
Managing editor Caroline Green
Project editor Amanda Redstone
Project managed by Emily Hooton and Karen Williams
Edited by Tracy Thomas
Proofread by Gaynor Spry
Cover design by Amparo Barrera
Cover artwork by David Roberts
Internal design by Ken Vail Graphic Design
Typesetting by Jouve India Private Limited
Illustrations by Advocate Art and Beehive Illustrations
Production by Robin Forrester

Printed and bound by Grafica Veneta S. P. A.

Acknowledgements
The publishers gratefully acknowledge the permissions granted to reproduce copyright material in the book. Every effort has been made to contact the holders of copyright material, but if any have been inadvertently overlooked, the Publisher will be pleased to make the necessary arrangements at the first opportunity.

HarperCollins*Publishers* Limited; Fraser Ross for an extract and artwork from *Jodie the Juggler* by Vivian French, illustrated by Beccy Blake, text copyright © Vivian French. HarperCollins*Publishers* Limited; Caroline Sheldon for an extract and artwork from *Worm Looks for Lunch* by Julia Donaldson, illustrated by Martin Remphry, text copyright © Julia Donaldson; HarperCollins*Publishers* Limited; David Higham Associates for *Kind Emma* by Martin Waddell, illustrated by David Roberts, text copyright © Martin Waddell; HarperCollins*Publishers*; Lucas Alexander Whitely Agency for *The Dolphin King* by Saviour Pirotta, illustrated by Fausto Bianchi, text copyright © Saviour Pirotta; HarperCollins*Publishers* for *World's Deadliest Creatures* by Anna Claybourne, copyright © Anna Claybourne; HarperCollins*Publishers*; Catchpole Agency for *When Arthur Wouldn't Sleep*, written and illustrated by Joseph Theobald, copyright © Joseph Theobald; HarperCollins*Publishers*; Caroline Sheldon; Juliette Lott for *The Pot of Gold* by Julia Donaldson, illustrated by Sholto Walker, text copyright © Julia Donaldson; HarperCollins*Publishers* for *Fire! Fire!* by Maureen Haselhurst.

The publishers wish to thank the following for permission to reproduce photographs. Every effort has been made to trace copyright holders and to obtain their permission for the use of copyright materials. The publishers will gladly receive any information enabling them to rectify any error or omission at the first opportunity.
(t = top, c = centre, b = bottom, r = right, l = left)

Cover & p 1 David Roberts

p36t Mirko Zanni/Photolibrary Group, p36bt Digital Vision/Getty Images, p36tc ANT/Photoshot, p36bc imageBROKER/Alamy, p36tb Nature Production/Naturepl, p36b Imagemore/Superstock, p40 Aratehortua/Shutterstock, p40 Kauriana/Shutterstock, p40 SeamartiniGraphicsMedia/Shutterstock.

Contents

1 Fun and games

1 **What did they say?**

Hello Jodie.
Come on in.

Nah not today

What?

Hey Jody I'm Sara
what's wrong

Wow, Sara!

② **What might Asif have said when the plate was broken?**

Ohh no.

Sounds and spelling Phonics

❶ **Write the words for these pictures.**

tray

cake

train

snail

chain

shared

❷ **Write three rhyming words in each list.**
The first one has been done for you.

wake	pain	may
bake		
cake	ake	
take		

3 The long vowel sound *a* can be spelled in three different ways. Give three examples.

- *ai* as in _____.

- *a–e* as in _____.

- *ay* as in _____.

Sounds and spelling Phonics

1 Write the words for these pictures.

_____   _____   _____

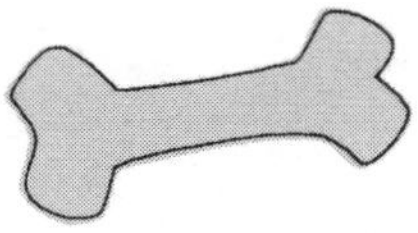

_____   _____   _____

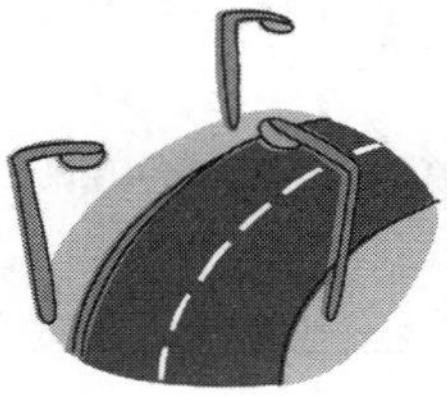

2 Write three rhyming words in each list, to match the spelling. The first one has been done for you.

float	mole	crow
coat	_____	_____
boat	_____	_____
moat	_____	_____

3

3 The long vowel sound *o* can be spelled in three different ways. Give three examples.

- *oa* as in _____.

- *o–e* as in _____.

- *ow* as in _____.

Reading and writing   Student's Book page 8

Mum took Jodie to the park. When he came back he told Asif what had happened. Complete his story.

Mum took me to the _____

to play _____.

Dom, Sue _____ Ash were in the park.

They _____ over to me.

They wanted to borrow my _____.

But first I _____ the ball.

It smashed some _____.

Mum was not _____.

She took me _____.

I said, "_____

_____."

4

Sounds and spelling Phonics

1 Write the words for the pictures.

_____ _____ _____

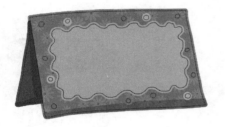  

_____ _____ _____

2 Add letters to make words.

__ar	__ark	__ard
_____	_____	_____
_____	_____	_____

3 Use the clues to work out each word. Circle the *ar* sound in each word.

● a round pastry case with a fruit filling _____

● the third month of the year _____

● a place where people buy and sell things _____.

Speaking and listening

1 Work with a partner. Talk about the words below.

2 Match the sentences to the word that describes the sound made.

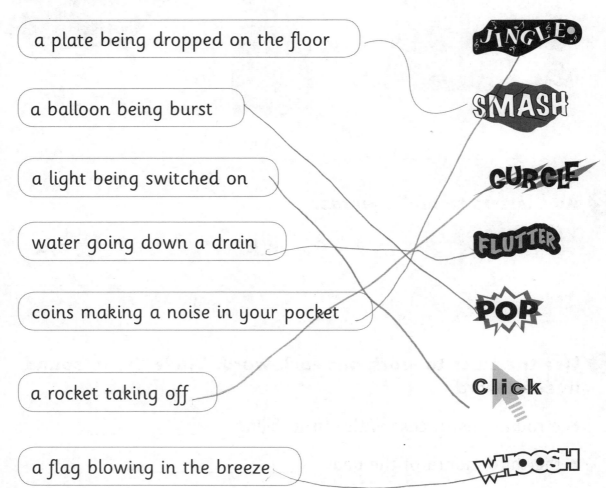

a plate being dropped on the floor

a balloon being burst

a light being switched on

water going down a drain

coins making a noise in your pocket

a rocket taking off

a flag blowing in the breeze

JINGLE

SMASH

GURGLE

FLUTTER

POP

Click

WHOOSH

1 Read the verse about sounds.

Sounds

The whistling of the wind,
The pattering of the rain,
The tapping of the hailstones
Upon the window pane.
The splashing of your gumboots
In the puddles of the lane,
The gurgling of the water
As it rushes down the drain.

2 Write the words that suggest sounds.

3 Write the words that rhyme.

4 Complete the verse.

The _____ of the cars
As they go _____by,
The _____ of the people
All _____ to stay dry.

Complete the table to show which activity broke the most things. One has been done for you.

	Activity	
	juggling	**football**
What Jodie broke	flowerpots	

2 The Olympics

Reading Student's Book pages 12–13

Write the name for each picture.

medals	olive wreath	flag
podium	Olympic torch	Olympic rings

flag

medals

Olympic torch

Olive wreath

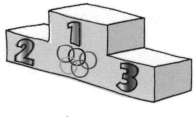

podium

Olympic Rings

Phonics

The flags of the medallists' countries are hoisted at the medal ceremony.

1 Use the letters in the box to make pairs of rhyming words.

b	p	c	m

hoist and _____   joint and _____

join and _____   foil and _____

2 Write the words.

t + oy _____   b + oy _____   j + oy _____

3 Read the words. Where do you hear the *oy / oi* sound – in the middle or at the end of the word?

Write the words in the table.

soil	toy	coin	boy	Roy	join

middle	end

Match the picture to the name of the sport. Circle the names of two sports that would be in the Winter Olympics.

hurdling

long jumping

skating

weightlifting

snowboarding

archery

Phonics

The men's football 'team' from Mexico won the gold medal at the 2012 Olympics.

1 Write an *ea* word to name each picture.

_____ ea _____   _____ ea _____   _____ ea _____

2 Add letters to make rhyming words.

–eep	–eel	–eet
_____	_____	_____
_____	_____	_____

3 **Choose the correct words to complete the sentences.**

- There are seven days in a _____ . | week   weak

- Hassan likes to _____ books. | reed   read

- Annie likes to splash in the _____ . | see   sea

Sounds and spelling | Phonics

1 **Write the words for the pictures.**

   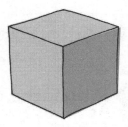

_____   _____   _____   _____

2 **Write the words with the long *u* sound.**
One has been done for you.

cut	fuss	grew	root	rut
true	tub	shoot	grub	mood
threw	mug	tube	cute	fuse

_____ grew _____   _____   _____

_____   _____   _____

_____   _____   _____

❸ Use the clues to work out the words:

● Something that helps to solve a problem. c _____

● 12 o'clock in the middle of the day. n _____

● Almost cold. c _____

● A solid shape with six square faces all the same size.

c _____

Reading and writing Student's Book page 18

❶ Match the shortened country name to its full name.

    (Jam)   (Kenya)

    (USA)   (Ethiopia)

    (Eth)   (Jamaica)

    (Ken)   (Great Britain)

                (GBR)   (United States of America)

② **Write the names of these countries in alphabetical order.**

Japan	France	Mexico	China
Italy	Brazil	Ethiopia	Australia

_____

_____

❸ **Write the names of these Olympic sports in alphabetical order.**

football	sailing	badminton	hockey
cycling		gymnastics	judo

_____

_____

Reading Student's Book page 18

Make your own Olympic medals.

What you need:

- round plastic lid
- paint brush
- acrylic paint (gold, silver and bronze)
- glitter glue pen
- ribbon
- strong sticky tape.

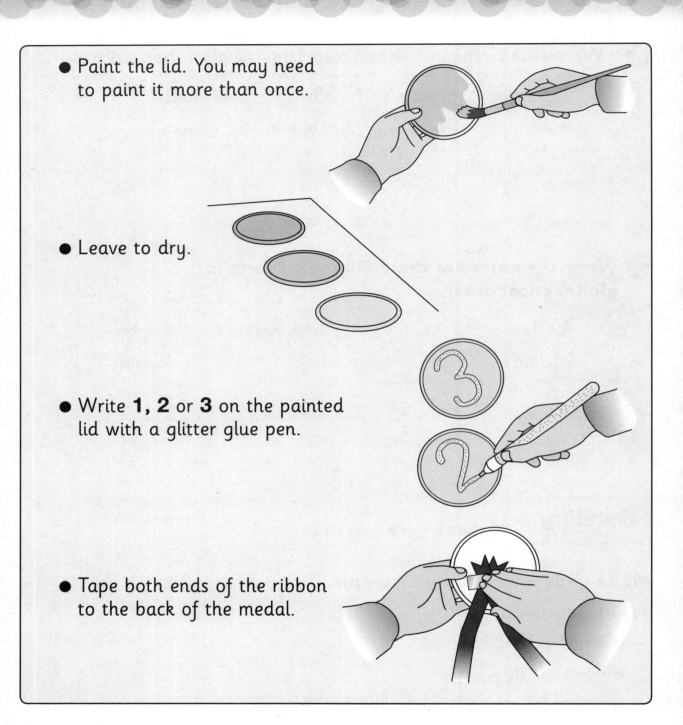

- Paint the lid. You may need to paint it more than once.

- Leave to dry.

- Write **1, 2** or **3** on the painted lid with a glitter glue pen.

- Tape both ends of the ribbon to the back of the medal.

3 What's for lunch?

Reading Student's Book page 25

Match the questions to each animal's answer.

"Hello Beetle. And what do you like to eat?"

"I like eating beetles."

"I like eating grass."

"Hello Bird. And what do you like to eat."

"I like eating leaves."

"Hello Rabbit. And what do you like to eat?"

"I like eating bark."

"Hello Deer. And what do you like to eat?"

"I like eating . . . WORMS!."

Writing Student's Book page 27

1. **Choose a name for a café.**

____

2. **Design and write a menu for your café.**

Café

Sounds and spelling — Phonics

1 Write the words for the pictures.

  9

_____   _____   _____   _____

2 Write three rhyming words in each list.

tie	fly	nine	light
_____	_____	_____	_____
_____	_____	_____	_____
_____	_____	_____	_____

3 The long vowel sound 'i' can be spelled in four different ways. Give four examples.

_ie_ as in _____.   _igh_ as in _____.

_y_ as in _____.   _i–e_ as in _____.

Phonics

Worm landed on the earth and wiggled safely
back into the ground.

1 Write the words for each picture.

_____ _____ _____

2 Write rhyming words.

house and _____ cloud and _____

mouth and _____ spout and _____

3 Write the words for each picture.

_____ _____ _____

4 Write rhyming words.

cow and _____ crown and _____

Imagine you are the bird in the book. Write your story.

After a play the audience applaud and talk to each other.
Write what you think they might say in the speech bubbles.

4 Kind Emma

Reading and writing   Student's Book pages 32–33

Choose words from the box to label each picture.

fire	spoon	door	house
bread	thing	table	soup

 _____

 _____

 _____

 _____

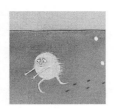 _____

 _____

 _____

 _____

Student's Book page 34

Match the beginning of each sentence with its ending.

Kind Emma lived all	a tiny thing scuttled in.
One night, a little voice called,	a very small spoon on the table.
She opened the door and	alone with no one to talk to.
She put a dish of hot soup and	the water was hot.
She hoped the tiny thing would come	"Oh, dear Emma, oh!"
Next morning, when Emma awoke ... the fire burned	out and eat if she left the room.

1 Choose letters from the box to make rhyming words. You can use a letter more than once.

c	h	b	st

torn _____ _____ _____

fork _____ _____

2 Choose letters from the box to make four words that rhyme with corn.

n	b	j	h	q	s	t	th

_____ _____ _____ _____

3 Which letters were not needed? _____

4 Complete the sentences with words ending in –er.

silver	brother	sister	shower	flower	winner

● There was a _____ of rain last night.

● The boy and girl are _____ and _____.

● The _____ has a lovely smell.

● The _____ won a gold medal.

● The person in second place won the _____ medal.

1 **Read the sentences. Circle the verbs.**

- Emma   lived   all   alone.
- She   opened   the   door.
- She   poked   the   fire.
- She   put   a   dish   of   hot   soup   on   the   table.
- She   left   the   room.

2 **Write the verbs to complete the sentences.**

- The fire _____ and the water was hot.
- The floor was _____ and the house was tidy and clean.
- The tiny thing _____ with Kind Emma.

3 **Choose one of the verbs from the box and write a sentence.**

opened	left	lived

_____

_____

_____

Reading and writing Student's Book page 37

1 Choose the correct words from the box to write under each picture.

| unzip | unpack | disappear | dislike | unlock | disagree |

_____   _____   _____

_____   _____   _____

2 Write the words from question 1 again.
Then write their opposites next to them.

| unzip ⟶ zip | _____ ⟶ _____ |

| _____ ⟶ _____ | _____ ⟶ _____ |

| _____ ⟶ _____ | _____ ⟶ _____ |

Number the sentences in the correct order (1 to 8) to match the story.

[ ] Emma opened the door and a tiny thing scuttled in.

[ ] Emma said, "Goodnight!" and left the room.

[ ] One night Emma heard a little voice.

[ ] She poked the fire to make it glow.

[ ] Next morning, when Emma awoke, the fire burned and the water was hot.

[ ] But the tiny thing stayed hidden.

[ ] Then she put a dish of hot soup and a small spoon on the table.

[ ] The tiny thing stayed with Emma for all the rest of her days.

Writing
Student's Book page 40

Write a review of the story. Use this form.

Book Review

Title

____

____

Author's name

____

____

Characters' names

____

____

Why I liked or did not like the book

____

____

____

My favourite part of the book

____

____

____

5 Animals and us

Draw a line to match each word to its definition.

hurl	to make a loud, high cry
spear	to plunge into water
scream	a long, stabbing weapon for throwing
dive	to make healthy
strange	to speak very softly
whisper	to throw forcefully
heal	unusual

1 Complete the words using the letters *ph*. Copy the words.

dol ____ in

_____

____ otogra ____

_____

tele ____ one

_____

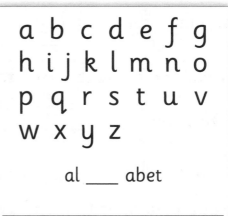

a b c d e f g
h i j k l m n o
p q r s t u v
w x y z

al ____ abet

_____

ele ____ ant

_____

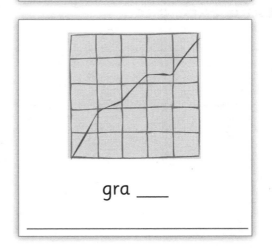

gra ____

_____

Sounds and spelling

Phonics

1 Add the suffix *–ful* to make new words.

• help	+	ful	=	helpful
• pain	+	ful	=	______
• hand	+	ful	=	______
• care	+	ful	=	______
• use	+	ful	=	______
• hope	+	ful	=	______
• play	+	ful	=	______

2 Choose the correct word to complete the sentences.

- Take good ______ of your bike. (care/careful)
- He was ______ when he rode his bike. (care/careful)

3 Choose two words from question 1 and write a sentence using each one.

______

______

______

______

Number the sentences in the correct order (1 to 8) to match the story.

☐ The animal screamed and dived beneath the waves.

☐ A strange knight rose out of the waves.

☐ Jean promised never to hunt dolphins again.

☐ Jean hurled his spear at a dolphin.

☐ The knight carried Jean down to the bottom of the sea.

☐ Jean helped the dolphin king.

☐ Suddenly, a fierce storm blew up.

☐ There, the dolphin king was waiting.

1 **Write the words in alphabetical order.**

dolphin	storm	boat	friend

_____

_____

_____

_____

waves	spear	knight

_____

_____

_____

2 **Find the words in the word search puzzle.**

w	b	x	s	u	z	k
d	o	l	p	h	i	n
w	a	v	e	s	y	i
c	t	j	a	q	u	g
s	t	o	r	m	v	h
f	r	i	e	n	d	t

dolphin

friend

waves

storm

boat

knight

spear

Draw lines to match the words to their meanings.

venom	a big group of insects
poisonous	harmful chemical injected when an animal bites you
swarm	sharp teeth which inject poison
tentacles	dangerous to eat or touch
fangs	unsafe
creature	long, dangly body parts used for feeding or moving about
dangerous	an animal, especially a non-human

Student's Book page 57

1 Tick the box showing which country or countries each creature can be found in.

	Africa	India	China	Australia	Middle East	Japan
spider (p3)						
scorpion (p5)						
cobra (p4)						
octopus (p7)						
jellyfish (p9)						

2 Read the chart to find out:

Which country has the most deadly creatures?

_____

Which countries have only one type of deadly creature?

_____

Which countries have more than one type of deadly creature?

_____

Student's Book page 58

1 Write the words. Mark the syllables. Write the number of syllables in brackets.

lizard   spider   octopus

_____ (   )   _____ (   )   _____ (   )

cobra   scorpion   frog

_____ (   )   _____ (   )   _____ (   )

2 Mark the syllables in these words.

| animal | spider | venom |

3 Write the two words that join to make 'jellyfish'.

_____   _____

4 Join the words to 'fish' to make new compound words. Write the words.

gold

star   fish   _____

sword   _____

                   _____

Write the name of each creature under the correct habitat.

whale   octopus   tiger   elephant

shark

giraffe

ocean	**jungle**
ice and snow	**underground**

polar bear

monkey

worm

penguin

meerkat

walrus

badger

armadillo

Writing
Student's Book page 56

Write a review of the book. Use this form.

Book Review

Title

____

Author's name

____

____

Why I liked or did not like the book

____

____

____

____

____

My favourite part of the book

____

____

____

____

____

____

7 When Arthur Wouldn't Sleep

Writing Student's Book page 64

Label each picture with the correct word from the box.

hippo	ladybird	Arthur	bee
Flora	grasshopper	sheep	butterfly

_____

_____

_____

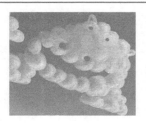

_____

Student's Book page 66

Who said it? Write the name next to the speech bubble.

Flora   ladybird   Arthur   hippo   grasshopper

Let's play jumping.

_____

It's bedtime. Time to go to sleep.

_____

Where do you want to go?

_____

I want to go where no one goes to sleep.

_____

This is your stop.

_____

Come with me.

_____

It's time for the Amazing Crazylegs Dancing Competition.

_____

And the winner is ... ARTHUR!

_____

I have to go now.

_____

Wake up Arthur. Time to get up!

_____

1 **Draw lines to match the words to their meanings.**

jump	to jump on one leg
mumble	to stare at
hop	to turn around in a circle
competition	to speak quietly and not clearly
twirl	to spring up
grumble	to leap
bounce	a contest
gaze	to complain

2 **Read the sentence in the box. Choose and write the sentence that has a similar meaning.**

They danced until their legs felt like jelly.

● They danced until their legs were very tired.
● They danced until it was time to eat jelly.

_____

_____

Sounds and spelling Phonics

1 **Add –ed to each word to make a new word.**

twirl + ed = ____twirled____   jump + ed = _____

start + ed = _____   want + ed = _____

wait + ed = _____   push + ed = _____

bang + ed = _____   rest + ed = _____

crash + ed = _____   park + ed = _____

land + ed = _____   play + ed = _____

melt + ed = _____   kick + ed = _____

2 **Look out for words that end in –e like 'dance'.**
Make each word into the past tense.

dance ➡ ____danced____   prance ➡ _____

bounce ➡ _____   grumble ➡ _____

Writing Student's Book page 68

Write the words that the characters said using speech marks. One has been done for you.

"I don't want to sleep," said
Arthur _____

I don't want to go to sleep.

_____
_____
_____

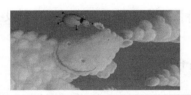

Where do you want to go?

_____
_____
_____

Come with me.

_____
_____
_____

... and the winner is ... ARTHUR!

_____
_____
_____

I have to go now.

1 Imagine you had a dream. Draw a picture of it.

2 Write about your dream.

8 The Pot of Gold

Writing | Student's Book page 76

Write a caption for each picture.
One has been done for you.

<u>a juicy peach</u>	_____ _____
_____ _____	_____ _____
_____ _____	_____ _____

Number the sentences in the correct order (1 to 8) to match the story.

☐ He gave Sandy and Bonny two coins and stayed for the night.

☐ At night, Sandy and Bonny went to get the gold.

☐ A little man tapped at the door.

☐ When they got home the little man had gone.

☐ The next day, Sandy saw a heap of gold coins.

☐ They hunted all night but they didn't find the gold.

☐ He left two gold coins on the table.

☐ He stuck his stick into the stones.

Imagine you are a newspaper reporter interviewing Sandy and Bonny about what had happened.

Write a list of questions that you would ask Sandy and Bonny.

Reading and writing

Student's Book page 85

Draw lines to match the words to their meanings.

helmet	used to gain entry into a building
jacket and trousers	protects the firefighter's head, neck and ears from getting burnt
axe	used to put out fires
hood	protects the firefighter's head from falling debris
hoses	protects the firefighter's body from extreme heat
gloves	supplies clean air to the firefighter
face mask	protects the firefighter's hands from burns and cuts

...und spelling

Student's Book page 87

1 **W... the two small words that make up these compound words.**

firefighters	________	+	________
fireworks	________	+	________
hosepipes	________	+	________
blowout	________	+	________
airships	________	+	________

2 **Write the words. Mark the syllables.**
Write the number of syllables.

	Write the word and mark the syllables	Number of syllables
dangerous		
helicopter		
forest		
powerful		

Match the beginning of each sentence with its ending.

Fires can be	land, at sea and from the air.
The firefighters put out flames	fast-fire cars might help to put out fires.
Firefighters put out fires on	fire boats with powerful hoses.
An oil well fire can burn	dangerous.
Big oil tanker fires need	like a huge, flaming torch.
In the future, giant airships, robots and	with jets of water from hosepipes.

Write the correct words to complete the glossary.

sirens   fire boat   jet skis   airships   water-bomb   oil well

Glossary

_____

large flying balloons with engines

_____

a large boat with powerful hoses to tackle oil tanker fires at sea

_____

small boats which are ridden like motorbikes

_____

a well which pumps up the black, sticky liquid that is used to make oil and petrol

_____

loud sounds that warn people of danger

_____

dropping water from the air

Reading and writing

Write items under each heading. Use the pictures to help and also think of as many others as you can.

firefighters' clothing	firefighters' equipment
where firefighters put fires out	what firefighters travel in

How well did I do?

■ I managed this unit   ● I did well in this unit   ▲ I did really well in this unit

Unit	■	●	▲
1 Fun and games			
2 The Olympics			
3 What's for lunch?			
4 Kind Emma			
5 Animals and us			
6 Staying safe			
7 When Arthur Wouldn't Sleep			
8 The Pot of Gold			
9 People who help us			